M000311624

The Land and People of

MALAYSIA AND BRUNEI

The Land and People of®
MALAYSIA AND BRUNEI

by John S. Major

HarperCollins*Publishers*

Country maps by Robert Romagnoli

Every effort has been made to locate the copyright holders
of all copyrighted materials and to secure the necessary
permission to reproduce them. In the event of any questions
arising as to their use, the publisher will be glad to make
necessary changes in future printings and editions.

Excerpt on page 168 from *Island of Bali* by Miguel Covarrubias.
Copyright 1936, 1937 by Alfred A. Knopf, Inc.
and renewed 1964, 1965 by Rosa Covarrubias.
Reprinted by permission of Alfred A. Knopf, Inc.

THE LAND AND PEOPLE OF
is a registered trademark of
HarperCollins Publishers

The Land and People of Malaysia and Brunei
Copyright © 1991 by John S. Major
Printed in the U.S.A. All rights reserved.
For information address HarperCollins Children's Books,
a division of HarperCollins Publishers,
10 East 53rd Street, New York, NY 10022.

Library of Congress Cataloging-in-Publication Data
Major, John S., date
  The land and people of Malaysia and Brunei/by John S. Major.
  p.   cm. — (Portraits of the nations)
  Includes bibliographical references and index.
  Summary: Introduces the history, geography, people, culture,
government, and economy of Malaysia and Brunei.
  ISBN 0-06-022488-6.—ISBN 0-06-022489-4 (lib. bdg.)
  1. Malaysia—Juvenile literature. 2. Brunei—Juvenile literature.
[1. Malaysia. 2. Brunei.] I. Title. II. Series.
DS592.M185 1991   90-20124
959.5—dc20   CIP
                                        AC

1 2 3 4 5 6 7 8 9 10
First Edition

Photographs by the author unless otherwise credited

For
STEPHEN

Contents

THE WORLD

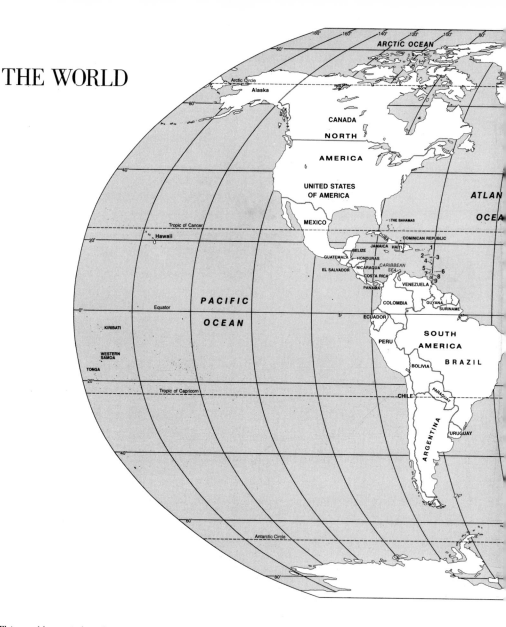

This world map is based on a projection developed by Arthur H. Robinson. The shape of each country and its size, relative to other countries, are more accurately expressed here than in previous maps. The map also gives equal importance to all of the continents, instead of placing North America at the center of the world. *Used by permission of the Foreign Policy Association.*

Legend

—— International boundaries

-------- Disputed or undefined boundaries

Projection: Robinson

| 0 | 1000 | 2000 | 3000 Miles |
| 0 | 1000 | 2000 | 3000 Kilometers |

Caribbean Nations

1. Anguilla
2. St. Christopher and Nevis
3. Antigua and Barbuda
4. Dominica
5. St. Lucia
6. Barbados
7. St. Vincent
8. Grenada
9. Trinidad and Tobago

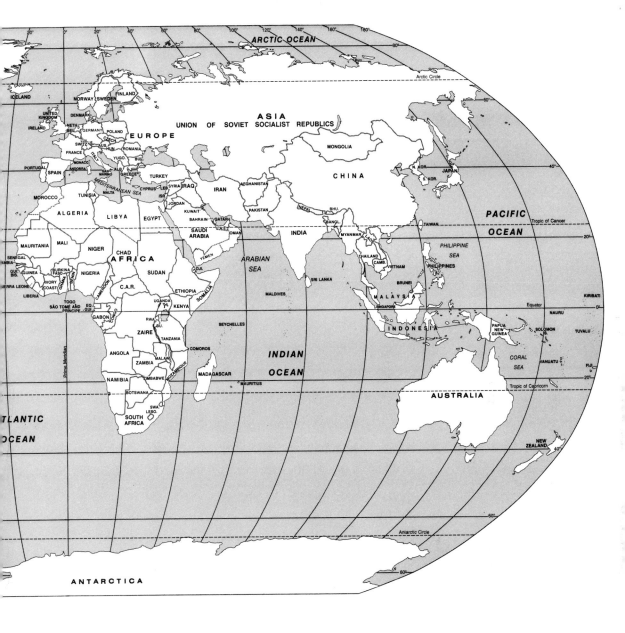

Abbreviations

ALB.	—Albania	C.A.R.	—Central African Republic	LEB.	—Lebanon	SWA.	—Swaziland
AUS.	—Austria	CZECH.	—Czechoslovakia	LESO.	—Lesotho	SWITZ.	—Switzerland
BANGL.	—Bangladesh	DJI.	—Djibouti	LIE.	—Liechtenstein	U.A.E.	—United Arab Emirates
BEL.	—Belgium	EQ. GUI.	—Equatorial Guinea	LUX.	—Luxemburg	YUGO.	—Yugoslavia
BHU.	—Bhutan	GER.	Germany	NETH.	—Netherlands		
BU.	—Burundi	GUI. BIS.	—Guinea Bissau	N. KOR.	—North Korea		
BUL.	—Bulgaria	HUN.	—Hungary	RWA.	—Rwanda		
CAMB.	—Cambodia	ISR.	—Israel	S. KOR.	—South Korea		

Mini Facts: Malaysia

OFFICIAL NAME: Federation of Malaysia

LOCATION: Southeast Asia: the Malay Peninsula and the northern portion of the island of Borneo. Borders on Thailand in the north and Singapore in the south on the Malay Peninsula; on Indonesia and Brunei in Borneo.

AREA: 127,320 square miles (329,757 square kilometers)

CAPITAL: Kuala Lumpur

POPULATION: 17,339,000 (1990): cities and towns 38%, rural 62%. Population growth rate, 2.4%.

MAJOR LANGUAGES: Malay, Chinese, English, Tamil and other Indian languages, and numerous tribal languages

RELIGIONS: Islam, Chinese Popular Religion (including Confucianism, Buddhism, and Daoism), Hinduism, Christianity, indigenous religions

TYPE OF GOVERNMENT: Constitutional monarchy

HEAD OF STATE: King; rulers of nine hereditary royal houses serve in rotation for five-year term as king

HEAD OF GOVERNMENT: Prime Minister

PARLIAMENT: Bicameral, with 58-member Senate and 177-member House of Representatives, elected for maximum term of five years

ADMINISTRATIVE SUBDIVISIONS: 13 states: 11 in Peninsular Malaysia, 2 in Borneo

ADULT LITERACY: 80% (est.)

LIFE EXPECTANCY: Female, 72.7 years; male, 68 years

MAIN PRODUCTS: *Agriculture and Forestry*—rubber, palm oil, timber, pepper, rice. *Mining and Petroleum*—tin, petroleum, natural gas. *Industry*—electrical products, petroleum refining, rubber production, palm oil refining, textiles, food processing, other light manufacturing.

CURRENCY: Ringgit (also known as Malaysian dollar). M$1.00 = US$.37 (1990)

Mini Facts: Brunei

OFFICIAL NAME: Brunei Darussalam

LOCATION: Southeast Asia, on northern coast of Borneo. Border with state of Sarawak, Malaysia, by which it is surrounded and bisected.

AREA: 2,226 square miles (5,765 square kilometers)

CAPITAL: Bandar Seri Begawan

POPULATION: 316,565 (1988): cities and towns, 59%; rural, 41%

LANGUAGES: Malay, English, Chinese

RELIGIONS: Islam, Chinese Popular Religion (including Confucianism, Buddhism, and Daoism), Christianity

TYPE OF GOVERNMENT: Constitutional monarchy (Sultanate)

HEAD OF STATE: Sultan

HEAD OF GOVERNMENT: Prime Minister

PARLIAMENT: Executive Council and Legislative Council, appointed by the Sultan

ADMINISTRATIVE SUBDIVISIONS: 4 districts

ADULT LITERACY: 80%

LIFE EXPECTANCY: 74 years (male-female average)

MAIN PRODUCTS: Petroleum and natural gas

CURRENCY: Brunei dollar. Par value with Singapore dollar. B$1.00 = US$.54 (1990)

A Note on Spelling,
Pronunciation, and Usage
of Malay

Despite efforts made in recent years by authorities in Malaysia, Brunei, and Indonesia to promote a uniform spelling of Standard Malay in those countries, there continues to be considerable variation in the spelling of Malay words in the Latin alphabet. In this book, all Malay words are spelled according to standard recommended modern usage; some words may therefore differ in spelling from the spelling used in older books. In particular, many older works on Southeast Asia used Indonesian spellings that are now obsolete, for example, "dj" instead of "j," and "tj" instead of "c." For geographical terms, this book generally follows the usage of *The New York Times Atlas of the World,* so that, for example, we use Johor instead of the older Johore, Terengganu instead of the older Trengganu. The new standard spelling "Melaka" is used for the city and state of that name, but the older spelling is retained for the Strait of Malacca, as well as in quotations from old sources that refer to the city itself. Place names on the historical map on page 105 are given in the form current at the turn of the twentieth century.

The pronunciation of Standard Malay is in general rather easy. Consonants are pronounced as in English, with the exception of "c," which is always pronounced as a hard "ch." For example, the word *campur* (mixed) is pronounced "champur." Vowels are generally pronounced as in Spanish: A is "ah," as in "father"; i is pronounced as a long "e," as in "ski"; o is pronounced "oh," as in "open"; and u is pronounced "oo," as in "food." The pronunciation of e is variable, however, with several sounds assigned to the same letter. It is sometimes pronounced as a long "a," as in "ale," sometimes as a short "e," as in "elbow," and sometimes it is nearly silent. For example, the word *enak* (delicious) is pronounced "a-nahk"; the word *lepas* (free) is pronounced "leh-pas"; the word *terimakasi* (thank you) is pronounced "tree-mah kah-see."

The word "Malay" presents special difficulties. It usually refers to the Standard Malay language, or to a native speaker of that language from the Malay Peninsula. But in phrases such as "the Malay languages," "Malay peoples," or "the Malay world," it refers to the family of closely related languages that includes Malay, but also (for example) Javanese, Iban, and Kadazan; to native speakers of those languages; and to the area of the world in which they live. In general, the reference should be clear from the context. "Malaya" refers to the Malay Peninsula as a political or geographical entity prior to the formation of the Malaysian Federation; "Malaysia" means the modern nation that includes the eleven Malay states of the Peninsula together with Sarawak and Sabah.

Malaysia and the Malay World

The Malay Peninsula stands astride one of the great crossroads of the world. For thousands of years, people, goods, and ideas have flowed south through the Peninsula from mainland Asia to the islands of Southeast Asia, and beyond them to the lands of Australasia (that is, New Guinea, Australia, and nearby islands). The Peninsula, a land highway from north to south, also forms the right bank of the Strait of Malacca, a water highway joining east to west; the Strait is the shortest and safest route between the Indian Ocean and the South China Sea. In 1515 Tomé Pires, a Portuguese merchant living in Melaka, described that city as the hub of world trade, rivaling even the great commercial centers of the Mediterranean: "Whoever is Lord of Malacca has his hands on the throat of Venice." In other words, by controlling Melaka the Portuguese could make sure that all European commerce with Asia was routed around Africa, bypassing Venice altogether.

Malaya and its adjacent waters have for countless centuries played a key role in the spread of human populations and cultures across a wide area—a role comparable to that of the Mediterranean Sea in the Greek and Roman world, the Bering Strait between Siberia and North America, or the broad steppe belt across Central Asia linking Europe and the Far East.

Beginning sometime around seven thousand years ago, many historians have suggested, the ancestors of the Malay people moved from an original homeland somewhere in the lowlands of Cambodia and the Mekong Delta of Vietnam (or perhaps, according to other authorities, in the mountains along the China-Vietnam border) south to the Malay Peninsula and to the island of Sumatra on the west bank of the Strait of Malacca. In successive slow surges of migration prompted by competition for land and resources, population pressures, and the opportunity of new lands to settle, communities spread to the various islands of what today are East Malaysia and Indonesia.

Relatively isolated from each other, those communities gradually developed into separate ethnic groups, with their own languages (all descended from the original language of the ancestors of the Malay people), customs, and lifestyles. Some groups remained hunter-gatherers, relying on the abundant plant and animal resources of the forested mountains and valleys for all the necessities of life. Some became farmers, others fisherfolk. Some who lived near the coasts became mariners, skilled at sailing their outrigger canoes over immense distances; eventually, descendants of these mariners spread their languages and cultures more than halfway around the globe, from Madagascar near the eastern coast of Africa to Easter Island off the western coast of South America.

The Malay Language

The Malay language, *Bahasa Melayu*, belongs to the
Malayo-Polynesian language family, just as, for example, English
belongs to the Indo-European language family. As the
Indo-European languages reflect the spread of the original
Indo-European people from a homeland near the Caspian Sea over a
period of many centuries, so also the hundreds of languages in the
Malayo-Polynesian language family reflect the migrations of
descendants of the original ancestors of the Malays. Today,
Malayo-Polynesian languages are spoken everywhere from
Madagascar, near the coast of Africa, through Malaysia and
Indonesia, to the Philippines and Taiwan (as well as the mountains
of Cambodia and Vietnam) in the north, Polynesia in the east, and
New Zealand in the south.

The Malay language itself, originally spoken in the Malay
Peninsula and in nearby portions of the island of Sumatra, is the
most prominent and widespread member of a sub-family of
Malayo-Polynesian languages known as the Malay language group.
Standard Malay is therefore closely related to the numerous other
languages spoken by ethnic groups in different parts of the country,
such as Iban, Kadazan, Bajau, and Melanau. A simplified form of
Malay, sometimes called "bazaar Malay," was used for hundreds of
years as a language of trade among the islands of the East Indies.
This allowed people who spoke a great many different languages,
including Javanese, Sundanese, Bugis, and others in the Malay
language group, to conduct their affairs in a common tongue. There
are many other examples of trade languages in world history.
Swahili originated as a trade language in East Africa, and English
has become the language of world commerce today. As a result of

its use in commerce, Malay spread widely throughout the region. Now, Standard Malay, Brunei Malay, and Indonesian are essentially the same language, differing from each other only in a small amount of local vocabulary. For example, "office" is *pejabat* in Malay and Brunei Malay, but *kantor* in Indonesian; "busy" is *sibuk* in Malay and Indonesian, but *gagau* in Brunei Malay.

Because the Malay Peninsula and the Strait of Malacca have served as a "crossroads of Asia" for hundreds of years, the Malay language has absorbed a great deal of vocabulary from the languages of other peoples who have come to the region for trade or conquest. Standard Malay includes words from Sanskrit and other Indian languages (*agama*, religion), Chinese (*cap*—pronounced "chop"—literally seal, but in ordinary use, brand name), Arabic (*hukum*, law), Dutch (*ya*, yes), Portuguese (*pesta*, festival), and English (*tilpun*, telephone).

Standard Malay, derived from "bazaar Malay," is well suited as a common language to unite the diverse ethnic population of Malaysia (and Indonesia as well), because it is easy to pronounce and has a simple grammatical structure. Most vocabulary is built from root words by means of a regular set of prefixes and suffixes. For example, the root word *jual*, "selling," gives a whole family of vocabulary dealing with trade:

jualan, merchandise, goods
menjual, to sell
menjualkan, to sell something for someone else
penjual, a merchant
penjualan, sales, trade, turnover
dijual, for sale
terjual, sold out

The written form of the Malay language also reflects the influence of external cultures on the Malay world. In ancient times—beginning perhaps around 1200 years ago—Malay, along with related languages such as Javanese, was written with a script derived from Sanskrit, brought to Malaya by Indian traders. After around A.D. 1500, with the coming of Islam, Arabic script replaced Sanskrit for writing Malay; Arabic script continues in use today for religious purposes, and sometimes also for legal documents; it is still taught in public schools. But in the twentieth century the Latin alphabet began to replace Arabic letters for writing Malay, and it is now the most common way of writing the language.

The history of the Malay people is a history of diffusion, of spread from a small homeland to an immense island world stretching from the Indian Ocean to the Pacific. The Malay Peninsula, along with Sumatra and Java, remained the ancient heartland of the wider Malay world, seen by its own people as the fountainhead of the Malay language, culture, and ethnic identity.* But on the other hand, as the Malay peoples spread into a much larger world, the larger world also came to Malaya. Tomé Pires described merchants arriving there from as far away as Egypt and Armenia, as well as Arabia, India, and China. The ethnic diversity of Malaysia and Brunei today reflects their long history as a focus for maritime trade throughout the Old World. The peoples of Malaysia, and

---

*"Ethnic identity" means those beliefs, practices, or ideas that make a person a member of a particular ethnic group. "National identity" means those beliefs, practices, or ideas that make a person identify with a particular nation. In North America a person might be ethnically Ukranian, Spanish, or Senegalese, but also nationally American or Canadian. Whether ethnic identity or national identity will be more important depends on the individual.

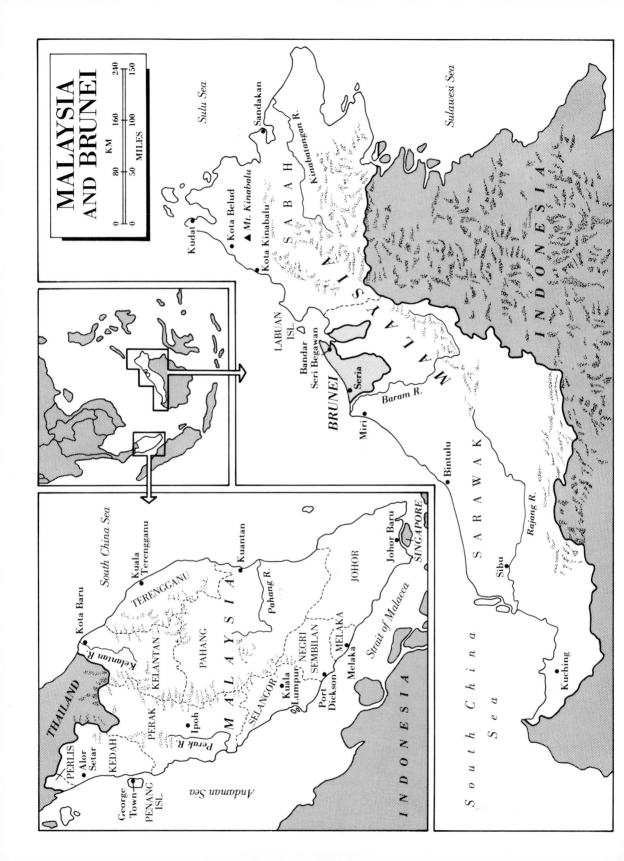

to a lesser extent Brunei, include not only ethnic Malays and their close relatives, but also Chinese, Indians, and even a few people of European and Arab ancestry.

The outside world intervened in another way as well. The creation of modern nation-states in the East Indies came about almost entirely through the influence of European colonial powers. Until the twentieth century there were almost no countries as we know them in this part of the world. The very concept of the "nation-state" was imported from Europe, along with new technologies and political and economic ideas. What had been a world of small kingdoms, tribal domains,* and far-flung trade networks was transformed into a world of nations with boundaries that followed colonial patterns rather than local political and ethnic ones. Malaysia was created by federating Sarawak and Sabah with the old Malay kingdoms of the Peninsula, adding millions of tribal peoples to the nation's population; Brunei survived as a tiny remnant of a once-powerful sultanate.

The Malay-speaking peoples are dispersed throughout the East Indies, though they have held on to their heartland in the Peninsula. Large numbers of Chinese and Indians have immigrated to the Peninsula and other parts of the East Indies. Many tribal peoples have been incorporated within the modern boundaries of Malaysia. These forces have combined to create an exceptionally difficult problem of Malaysian national identity. Anyone who stands for a few minutes on a busy street corner in downtown Kuala Lumpur today will see a bewildering range of pedestrians pass by—Chinese businessmen, Malay workers, elderly

---

*While some anthropologists object to the use of the word "tribe" in the context of Southeast Asia, it is used in this book as a convenient way of referring to groups of nonindustrialized (and, in some cases, nonagricultural) people linked by ties of kinship, language, and self-identification, and organized socially and politically in networks of villages or other small groups, in territories not defined by rigid boundaries. No suggestions of "primitiveness" or "backwardness" are implied or intended.

Indians dressed in saris and dhotis accompanied by their grandchildren in neat school uniforms, Kadazan merchants visiting from Sabah, European tourists, Japanese industrialists, and many more. "Unity amidst diversity" is both the noblest goal and the greatest challenge facing Malaysia today.

The Malays

The Malay people proper form a slight majority of the people of the Malay Peninsula, and a large majority of the population of Brunei. In Malaysia, however, the question of "who is a Malay?" is not always easy to answer. A common working definition holds that a Malay is a Muslim and a native speaker of Malay whose immediate ancestors came from the Malay Peninsula. By that standard, however, many Malays of Brunei, Sarawak, and Sabah would not qualify; rather than having ancestral roots in the Peninsula, they are descended from native peoples who gradually substituted Malay for their own language after converting to Islam. Malays, by any definition, form only a minority of the population of Sarawak and Sabah, concentrated mainly in the cities and towns. Moreover, because the Malay Peninsula is divided among eleven states, reflecting the old sultanates of premodern times, Malay ethnic identity is itself somewhat fragmented. Many peninsular Malays regard themselves as, for example, people of Johor or of Perak, not as members of some abstract group called "Malays"—rather as some Americans prefer to think of themselves as Californians or Texans. The problems of Malay ethnic identity are overcome to some extent by the use of the catch-all term *bumiputra,* or "son of the soil," which includes all Malaysian speakers of Malay-group languages, from urban Malays to forest Ibans.

Conventional wisdom in Malaysia holds that the cities are Chinese, the villages are Malay. As with most conventional wisdom, this is not

Bajau children at a water village near Kota Kinabalu, Sabah.

the whole truth, but it contains a large amount of truth. The *kampung* is the center of Malay life; literally the word means village, but it can also signify a neighborhood within a city—in either case, it is a small, tightly knit community united by ties of kinship, marriage, or neighborliness, where consensus, compromise, and traditional values reign supreme.

In Malaysia, Malays dominate government and agriculture, but (despite "affirmative action" laws favoring *bumiputras*) play a relatively small role in commerce and industry. In the countryside of West Malaysia, Malays are likely to be farmers, tending vegetable farms or small holdings of rubber or oil-palm trees, or fishermen; in the cities, they are often civil servants, laborers, transport workers, or industrial workers. A small number of Malays have risen to the national elite, either by descent from the old aristocracy, which still dominates the

The Kris

Much more than simply a weapon, the type of dagger known as a *kris* is a symbol of manhood, honor, and ethnic identity throughout the Malay world. Each region of Malaysia and Indonesia has its own distinctive style of *kris*, but in general a *kris* is a stabbing knife, with a blade about six to fifteen inches long, thin but flaring out to a very wide base, and with a short, curved handle. The blade of a *kris* is often wavy rather than straight; this has the practical function of making a wider and more dangerous wound than that caused by a straight-bladed dagger, but it also is said to symbolize the power of the cobra that the serpentine blade resembles.

The classic *kris* is a beautiful example of the traditional swordsmith's art. The blade is made of alternating layers of hard and soft steel, folded over and over again in the hot fire of the forge, in a technique rather like that found in the samurai sword of

highest levels of government and the military to a surprising degree, or by membership in the new aristocracy of commercial wealth. In general, though, if the *kampung* belongs to the Malays, the *kota* (city) belongs to the Chinese.

The Chinese

People of Chinese ancestry make up about a third of the population of West Malaysia, nearly a third of the population of Sarawak, one sixth

Japan; repeated foldings and forgings create a blade that is both flexible and sharp. In traditional Malay society, the makers of *krises* were regarded almost as sorcerers, not simply smiths. Before making a blade, they underwent complicated rituals of fasting and purification, and often cast spells to make their daggers more powerful.

Popular belief in the Malay world attributes many kinds of magic to the *kris*. Some blades are believed to obey their masters' commands, flying through the air to stab a distant enemy; others have the reputation of having turned on their owners when they tried to use them for evil purposes. A fine *kris* will be handed down from father to son within a family for generations, and is often the family's most precious possession; the heirloom *kris* of a king or aristocrat is the most potent emblem of his authority. In the modern world, the mystical significance of the *kris* makes it an instantly recognizable symbol of Malay ethnic identity and national independence.

of the population of Sabah, and one fifth of the population of Brunei. Throughout Malaysia and Brunei, every city has its Chinatown. Descendants of merchants who settled in the region many centuries ago, or (predominantly) of "coolies" who were imported by the British to work as contract laborers in mines and on plantations beginning in the nineteenth century (just as other Chinese were brought to America as miners and railroad workers around the same time), the Chinese of Malaysia and Brunei are by no means a homogeneous group. Their ancestors came from various provinces of South China, and they speak

a variety of Chinese dialects; some practice Buddhism, some Daoism, others one form or another of the mixture of Confucianism, Buddhism, and Daoism known only as "Chinese popular religion"; a few have converted to Islam or Christianity.

Overwhelmingly urban, especially on the Malay Peninsula, the Chinese are dominant in commerce and industry, and they have united as an ethnic group, despite their own diverse roots, in the face of discrimination at the hands of the Malay majority. The largest minority group in Malaysia, the Chinese have traditionally been regarded by the Malays with envy and suspicion because of their economic success. Yet just as not all Malays are peasants and workers, not all Chinese are rich merchants. There are Chinese farmers, miners, and plantation workers, some of them quite poor, and a Chinese urban working class. These people are doubly victimized, both by their own poverty and by the stereotype that says all Chinese are urban and rich. Moreover, not all Malaysian Chinese are conspicuously Chinese anymore; the Straits Chinese, residents of Melaka and other cities on the Strait of Malacca for hundreds of years, have developed a distinctive local culture that is as much Malay as it is Chinese.

Yet the stereotype of the Chinese as a rich urban merchant or professional is sufficiently true to make it be believed by Malays and Chinese alike. Raised in a community that values commerce and education as the road to success, and not "making waves" as the road to avoiding trouble, Malaysian Chinese have developed a culture of "permanent otherness," being secure and successful within their own community, but having constantly to prove their loyalty and patriotism to the nation as a whole.

Chinese businessmen, Kuala Lumpur. The Chinese of Malaysia are heavily concentrated in the country's large cities, and dominate industry and commerce.

The veteran journalist Ian Buruma recently recounted two conversations that capture the essence of Malay-Chinese mutual distrust. A Malay student told him,

Look around you, we are second-class citizens in our own country. The immigrants, yes, the immigrants get so many privileges here. Anything they want, they get. Can a Chinese be a cabinet minister in your country? Of course he can't. Here they have everything, own everything, all the business, Chinese.

Note that the student regards all Chinese in Malaysia as "immigrants," although most of them have been in the country for several generations. He also wrongly assumes that no person of Chinese ancestry could hold high political office in a Western democracy.

In contrast, a Chinese businessman spoke scornfully of the effects of the New Economic Policy "affirmative-action" laws designed to promote the economic status of Malays:

The *bumis* [*bumiputra*s], they get rich here from government loans. Then they build big houses. . . . They live in them and then they go bankrupt in them.

The Indians

Like the Chinese, some of the Indians of Malaysia are descended from merchants with centuries-deep roots in the country, while others are descendants of laborers recruited in India (mostly in what is now the southeastern state of Tamil Nadu) and brought to the country in the nineteenth and early twentieth centuries. Unlike the Chinese, relatively few Indians live in Sarawak, Sabah, and Brunei; they are concentrated mainly in West Malaysia. Among Malaysia's Indians, there is a clear distinction between the urban middle class and the rural poor. In such cities as Johor Baru and Kuala Lumpur, Indians are well represented in business and the professions, particularly law; many Indians also work as hotel keepers, restaurant owners, and small merchants. Malaysia's urban Indian population is very diverse, and includes Gujaratis, Malayalis, Punjabis, and many other Indian ethnic groups—a reflection of the diversity of India itself; some are Hindus, others Muslims. Nevertheless, the Indian population of Malaysia is overwhelmingly Tamil (some 85 percent of the total), and the Tamils are mainly rural and poor. Most, like their contract-laborer ancestors, are rubber workers; some are now small farmers. The persistent poverty and political powerlessness of these rural Indians is one of Malaysia's most severe social problems. As one Malaysian Indian politician recently put it, "It is not that the Malays have anything against us. It is just that as politicians, they are embroiled in their own unending troubles, so much so that they are not pressed to solve the problems of the Indians."

Indigenous Peoples

The population of the North Borneo states of Sarawak and Sabah is composed of members of a large number of native ethnic groups, almost all descended from Proto-Malay (the ancestors of the Malays) migrants who settled in Borneo thousands of years ago. Their languages are part of the Malay language group, but they are distinct both from Standard Malay and from each other. Until a generation or two ago, many of the indigenous peoples of Sarawak and Sabah lived traditional lives with little contact with the outside world; even today they retain a strong sense of distinctive ethnic and cultural identity.

The Iban (also called Sea Dayaks) are the largest ethnic group of Sarawak, comprising nearly one third of the population. The Iban are river and forest people, building communal longhouses on the banks of Borneo's winding rivers and using the waterways as highways for their long, slender canoes. Until recent times the Iban had the reputation of being fierce hunters—and headhunters—and, along the coast, seafarers and pirates. The great nineteenth-century naturalist Alfred Russel Wallace described his experience of staying in an Iban longhouse: "Near the landing-place we found a fine house, 250 feet long, raised high above the ground on posts, with a wide verandah and still wider platform of bamboo in front of it. . . . I slept very comfortable [*sic*] with half a dozen smoke-dried human skulls suspended over my head." Other longhouse peoples of Sarawak include the closely related Kayan and Kenyah tribes, the Bidayuh or Land Dayaks, and the Melanau, concentrated in the marshy coastlands. Some of these people have converted to Islam, others to Christianity, but many still maintain the old faith of their ancestors, worshipping a variety of household and nature gods. In the deep interior, the Murut and Penan are people of the forest, some of whom (like the Iban, Kenyah, and other tribal peoples of northern Borneo) still practice swidden agriculture* or live as hunter-gatherers, with little contact with the outside world.

Sabah, like Sarawak, has a diverse ethnic population. One example of this diversity is that the principal newspapers of Kota Kinabalu, the capital city, are trilingual: each edition contains pages in Malay, Kadazan, and English. The Kadazans are the largest ethnic group in Sabah. Formerly farmers in the hilly country around Mount Kinabalu, many now have moved to towns and cities to become merchants or urban workers. The majority of Kadazans are Christians. The Bajau, Sabah's second-largest ethnic group, live mainly near the coast. Sometimes known as "Sea Gypsies," the Bajau often live in villages built on stilts over the shallow waters of a harbor or river mouth, and work at fishing

---

*Swidden agriculture, sometimes misleadingly called "slash-and-burn" agriculture, involves cutting and burning a small clearing in the forest and raising crops there for several seasons, until the land begins to lose fertility. At that point, the clearing is allowed to revert to forest growth, and a new clearing is made elsewhere.

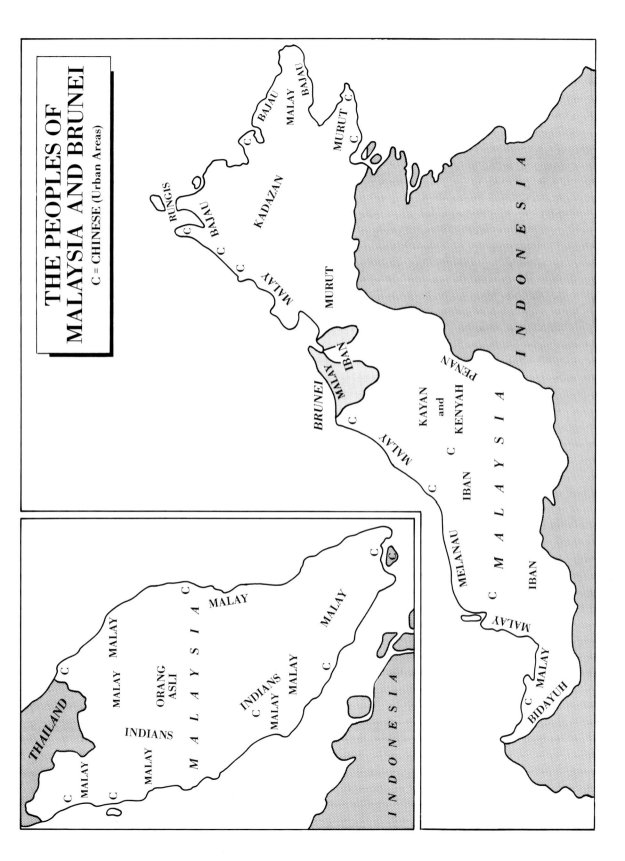

THE PEOPLES OF
MALAYSIA AND BRUNEI

C = CHINESE (Urban Areas)

and water transport. The novelist Joseph Conrad, visiting the area near the turn of the century, learned that "it is a common saying amongst the Malay race that to be a successful traveller and trader a man must have some Wajo [Bajau] blood in his veins." Inland, other Bajau are expert horse riders, and raise herds of cattle and water buffalo—they are the cowboys of Borneo. Many Bajau are Muslims, and a substantial minority are Christians. The Rungis of the northeastern tip of Sabah are closely related to the Kadazan; many still live in longhouses, and are farmers or plantation workers. As in Sarawak, the interior of Sabah supports a sparse population of Murut forest dwellers.

The Malay Peninsula has a small number of non-Malay aboriginal tribes, numbering perhaps 100,000 people in all. The Sakai live in small settlements in several parts of the Peninsula. The Semang people who live in forested areas in the states of Kedah and Perak, and the Pangan people of the interior of Kelantan, are both members of the Negrito ethnolinguistic group. These remnant populations of what the Malays call *orang asli*, or "original people," were left behind when most early tribal peoples were pushed out to eastern Indonesia and the southern Philippines as the Proto-Malays migrated to the Peninsula.

Even Brunei, although overwhelmingly Malay and Chinese in population, has a small minority of indigenous people—mainly Iban and Dusun (another name for the Kadazans)—in its forested hinterland.

Europeans, Eurasians, and Others

Malaysia's population includes a tiny minority of citizens of European ancestry, people who stayed on after the end of British colonial rule in

An old man at an Iban longhouse near Kuching, Sarawak. Most Iban still live in longhouses on the banks of Sarawak's rivers; young men often work as loggers, while women and older men tend the village gardens and pepper plantations.

1957. There is also a larger number of resident expatriates from Europe, America, and Japan, primarily employees of large multinational corporations. Larger still, but nevertheless a very small proportion of the entire population, is the so-called Eurasian community, made up of people of European-Malay, European-Chinese, or Arab-Eurasian descent. Most Malays have Arab names, and some of them claim descent from a long-distant Arab ancestor (though the vast majority are descendants of people who simply took Arab names when they converted to Islam centuries ago). In Melaka there is a small "Portuguese" community of people who resemble ethnic Malays in most respects except for their Catholic faith, their cuisine, and the Portuguese language spoken at home. In general, as Malaysia grows more urban and more industrialized, marriages between people of different ethnic communities are becoming more common, and this to a small extent is beginning to break down the rigid barriers of ethnicity that have characterized Malaysia up to the present time.

In Sabah, a different group of "other" people has arisen in recent times: Illegal immigrants from the Philippines and Indonesia, lured by jobs in the timber industry, now make up one sixth of the population, by some estimates. This is a cause of serious concern to the local government, but despite frequent identity checks and deportations of illegal aliens, the immigrant population continues to grow.

The rich diversity of Malaysia's population (and to a lesser extent that of Brunei as well) makes the country a fascinating mix of languages, cultures, and ways of life. But despite brave talk of being a "plural society," Malaysia is less a unified nation of many nationalities than it is an uneasy collection of isolated and mutually suspicious ethnic

Malay women at the city market, Kuala Terengganu, West Malaysia. The cities of the east coast of the Malay Peninsula have relatively small populations of Chinese and Indians; they retain some of the flavor of Malay village life.

groups. Differences of skin color, facial features, language, and religion are reflected in different patterns of residence, occupation, and social status. It *is* common for members of one ethnic group to have friends and acquaintances among members of other groups; to that extent, the concept of a plural society reflects a reality as well as a goal. Yet despite

Ethnic Groups of Malaysia and Brunei

	West Malaysia	Sarawak	Sabah	Brunei
Malay	55%	20%	15%	70%
Chinese	34%	29%	16%	20%
Indian	9%	*	*	*
Indigenous Groups	*	51%	52%	9%
	Sakai	Iban	Kadazan	Iban
	Semang	Bidayuh	Bajau	Dusun
	Pangan	Kayan/ Kenyah	Murut	
		Melanau	Rungis	
		Penan		
		Murut		
		Kelabit		
European/ Eurasian	*	*	*	*
Filipino/ Indonesian	?%	*	17%	*

* (under 1%)

A billboard advertising "1990—the Year to Visit Malaysia," celebrates the country's ethnic harmony amidst diversity: "The Malaysian People: United, Welcoming, Courteous."

such cordial pluralism, ethnic consciousness is ever present in most people's minds.

To a surprising degree, there is no such thing as a "typical" Malaysian. A Malay factory worker, a Tamil rubber plantation worker, a Chinese banker, an Indian lawyer, an Iban who lives in a longhouse but drives a bulldozer or wields a chain saw in a lumber camp, a Kadazan bus driver, a Bajau buffalo herder, and a Penan hunting with a blowgun are all "typical," and all as different from each other as the people of one nation can be.

The Land:
Geography and
Climate

Malaysia, slightly larger than New Mexico, consists of eleven small
states on the Malay Peninsula, and two very large states, Sarawak and
Sabah, in northern Borneo. West Malaysia and East Malaysia, as the
two parts of the country are called, are separated from each other by
the South China Sea. About 400 miles (650 kilometers) of open ocean
separates Johor Baru at the southern tip of the Malay Peninsula from
the western edge of Sarawak in Borneo; the distance from Perlis, in the
northwestern corner of West Malaysia, to Sandakan, on the eastern tip
of Sabah, is about 1,400 miles (2,260 kilometers).

Brunei, slightly larger than Delaware, is both surrounded by and split
in two by the Malaysian state of Sarawak. The present kingdom of
Brunei is, however, a modern remnant of what was once a far larger and

more powerful realm that ruled both Sarawak and Sabah as well as some of the islands of the southern Philippines.

The modern boundaries of Malaysia and Brunei do not make obvious geographical sense; what is worse, they have very little basis in ethnicity, religion, or local history. The forces that united the local kingdoms of the Malay Peninsula into a federation, that reduced the kingdom of Brunei to a mere shadow of its former extent, and that incorporated Sarawak and Sabah into Malaysia derived entirely from

Geography and Climate

HIGHEST MOUNTAINS   Mt. Tohon (West Malaysia): 7,173 feet (2,187 meters)
Mt. Kinabalu (Sabah): 13,428 ft. (4,094 m.)

LONGEST RIVERS   Pahang River (West Malaysia): 295 miles (477 kilometers) Kinabatangan River (Sabah): 349 mi. (563 km.) Rajang [or Rejang] River (Sarawak): 350 mi. (564 km.)

AVERAGE ANNUAL RAINFALL   95 inches (240 centimeters), Johor Baru, Malaysia; 99 in. (250 cm.), Brunei coast; 298 in. (750 cm.), Brunei interior

RAINY DAYS PER YEAR   175, Johor Baru, Malaysia

AVERAGE ANNUAL TEMPERATURE VARIATION   73°–88° Fahrenheit (23°–31° centigrade), Johor Baru, Malaysia; 73°–95° F. (23°–35° C.), Brunei

European conquests and rivalries in the age of colonialism. Geographically, West and East Malaysia are quite distinct from each other, while Brunei is geographically indistinguishable from the surrounding area of East Malaysia. The Malay Peninsula has more in common with Sumatra (its neighbor across the Strait of Malacca, but now part of Indonesia) than it has with Sarawak and Sabah; Sabah is historically and culturally linked with the southern islands of the Philippines. Nevertheless, all of Malaysia, and Brunei as well, also have some characteristics in common, including an equatorial climate, high mountain ranges, long coastlines punctuated by numerous sluggish rivers, an agricultural economy based on plantation crops, and abundant natural resources of forest products, minerals, and natural gas and petroleum.

The Malay Peninsula

The long, slender Malay Peninsula (the northern portion of which comprises part of Burma and Thailand) is dominated by a range of mountains that, with several offsets and breaks, extends down its entire length. This mountain range is one of several that originate in northeastern India, in the state of Assam, and spread out like the ribs of a fan throughout South China and Southeast Asia. These mountain ranges are a clue to the region's geological history; they were piled up when the Indian plate, one of the moving tectonic plates that form the earth's crust, collided with the Asian mainland, causing that larger plate to crumple up in mountain ridges and to rotate to the southeast.

Peninsular Malaysia (West Malaysia) occupies the widest and most mountainous portion of the Malay Peninsula. It is dominated by heavily forested mountains, and by the coastline; it has relatively little flat land except in narrow strips along the coast. Only in the south, in the states of Johor, Melaka, and the southern part of Pahang, is flat land more common than hills and mountains. In those areas, numerous small rivers have deposited silt from the mountains in large deltas that are overgrown by broad mangrove and nipa palm swamps.

The population of West Malaysia is crowded into towns and cities along the coasts and in the river valleys of the hilly piedmont. The western coast, close to the historic trade route of the Strait of Malacca, is much more heavily populated than the eastern coast. Only a few east-west roads connect the two coasts, because of the rugged mountainous terrain in between. Driving across the peninsula from west to east, one follows a road that rises rapidly through low hills to high mountains, through tunnels, and around switchbacks. Crossing the peninsular divide, the road descends more gently through a wider range of foothills to the narrow coastal plain.

Northern Borneo

Borneo, the third-largest island in the world (after Greenland and New Guinea), is dominated by an immense range of high mountains that runs roughly from southwest to northeast. The southern part of the island (the Indonesian province of Kalimantan) is ringed by vast, swampy coastal plains and river deltas, but northern Borneo—the part of the island shared by Sarawak, Brunei, and Sabah—is a land of forested mountains and numerous rivers. The western part of Borneo's central mountain range splits into southern and northern branches; Sarawak's border with Kalimantan follows the ridgeline of the northern branch from west to east until it reaches the junction point of the two branch ranges. From there it follows the ridgeline of the main range northeast and north until it touches the coast. The southern border of Sabah runs almost directly from west to east along a line that separates the mountainous northeastern tip of Borneo from the lowlands to the south.

Mount Kinabalu

A towering granite massif 13,428 feet (4,094 meters) tall, Mount Kinabalu in Sabah is the highest mountain between the Himalayas and the Maoke Range of New Guinea. Traditionally the mountain was regarded as a sacred place by the Kadazan people who live in the surrounding hills; its name is said to derive from a Kadazan phrase meaning "resting place of the dead." Today Mount Kinabalu is the centerpiece of one of Malaysia's most famous national parks; the strenuous hike to the mountain's summit is a popular tourist attraction.

Although Mount Kinabalu is located just a few degrees north of the equator, its great height creates zones of climate and vegetation that range from tropical to subarctic. Near the mountain's base are steaming tropical jungles filled with orchids, vine-draped trees, and hundreds of species of butterflies. At around 6,000 feet, tropical vegetation yields to a forest of oak trees; at 7,000 feet, the oak forest is replaced by a "cloud forest" of moss-draped pine trees and vinelike bamboos, interspersed with boggy patches of moss and carnivorous pitcher plants. At 8,500 feet the trail cuts through a nearly impenetrable tangle of rhododendron bushes. Above 9,500 feet only dwarf species of trees and bushes can survive; above the tree line, at 11,000 feet, alpine meadow gradually yields to the bare rock of the summit. Mount Kinabalu is not quite high enough to be permanently snowcapped, but a thick layer of frost coats the summit rock each morning.

Kinabalu National Park is recognized by naturalists throughout the world as a treasure house of species of animals, birds, insects, and plants, many of which are found nowhere else on earth.

Mount Kinabalu looms over the flat grazing lands of Bajau country in Sabah.

Although Brunei is tiny in comparison with Sarawak and Sabah, its geography provides a fair sample of that of northern Borneo as a whole. In its southeasternmost corner, Brunei includes a portion of Borneo's central mountain range, with peaks rising as high as 6,000 feet (1,850 meters). Streams arising in those heavily forested mountains rush rapidly downhill over waterfalls and through rapids, before becoming slower and broader in the foothills. The description of the nineteenth-century naturalist Alfred Russel Wallace still holds true: "Large trees stretch out their arms across the stream, and the steep, earthy banks are clothed with ferns. . . ." This is Iban country; the Iban, or Sea Dayaks, build their longhouses on the high riverbanks and use the rivers themselves as highways for their long, slender dugout boats.

Near the coast, the rivers become broader still and meander sluggishly through coastal marshes. The riverbanks disappear beneath broad and impenetrable belts of nipa palm, which grows in shallow water, and mangrove trees, whose stiltlike roots elevate them above the tidal mud flats. Here the rivers are inhabited more by crocodiles than by people. The only signs of human life are an occasional plank path connecting a river dock with the forest hidden hundreds of yards behind the palms and mangroves, and small settlements of stilt houses built, like the mangroves themselves, over the shallow water.

The rivers of Brunei seem to merge almost imperceptibly with the sea, in a swampy coastline broken only rarely by sandy beaches. In his novel *The Rescue,* Joseph Conrad described the northern Borneo coast as viewed from the sea in the late nineteenth century: "The coast . . . has no distinctive features. It is without form. It stretches away without cape or bluff. . . . It presents to view only a narrow band of earth that appears crushed flat upon the vast level of waters by the weight of the sky."

Today, of course, the rivers and coastline of Brunei also give evidence of very modern human activity. The gleaming modern city of Bandar Seri Begawan has spread beyond the old town of stilt houses built over the Brunei River to occupy the flatlands and hills on both banks of the river; and along the coast the monotonous landscape that Conrad described is broken by offshore oil rigs and tanker loading docks.

If Brunei can be seen as a "northern Borneo in miniature," the reality of Sarawak and Sabah is nevertheless much more dramatic. In those states of East Malaysia, the mountains are far higher and more rugged, the rivers far longer and broader. Sabah's Mount Kinabalu, at over 13,000 feet (4,000 meters) the highest mountain for more than a thousand miles in any direction, rises from a steaming equatorial jungle at its base to near-arctic conditions at its summit. Sarawak's Rajang River, about 350 miles (564 kilometers) long, originates in the heart of

A branch of the Rajang, Malaysia's longest river, winds through the coastal plains and mangrove swamps of Sarawak. A town is visible where a smaller river joins the main stream at the upper right.

Borneo's central mountain range and crashes through seemingly endless rapids before beginning a slower descent through the rain forest. Its broad, meandering lower reaches are plied by river steamers between the coast and the town of Kapit, about 150 miles (240 kilometers) inland.

The Climate

Most visitors to Malaysia would agree that the country's climate can be summed up in a single word: Hot. Throughout the country, temperatures range from overnight lows in the upper 60's or low 70's Fahrenheit (about 20° centigrade) to daytime highs in the upper 80's or low 90's (up to about 35° C.). The only exceptions are in mountainous areas, where temperatures are generally lower, especially at night; on the highest peaks, overnight temperatures can be below freezing. The mountain resorts of Fraser Hill and the Cameron Highlands near Kuala Lumpur are testimony to Malaysia's relentless tropical heat; they were developed by British colonial rulers in the nineteenth century as "hill stations" where Europeans could escape to find some welcome coolness.

With tropical heat comes tropical humidity, especially in the coastal areas. Rain showers are common, and there are about 180 rainy days in every year. Most noticeably in Peninsular Malaysia, the year is divided into wet and dry seasons, caused by the effects of the monsoon winds of Southeast Asia. Prevailing winds blow from the northeast from November to April, and from the southwest from May to October; rain is especially heavy in the weeks when the winds shift direction, bringing occasional spells of cooler weather. Blistering heat and dry weather characterize the mid-monsoon periods. Sabah is sometimes known as "The Land Below the Winds," because it (along with the rest of northern Borneo) lies south of the steady temperate-zone trade winds that aided navigation in the South China Sea in the days of sailing ships;

there, too, the shifting monsoons bring fierce tropical storms.

The heat, humidity, and abundant rainfall that characterize Malaysia's climate are also responsible for its most conspicuous natural resource, the tropical rain forest.

The Forest

Before the dawn of the modern era of chain saws and international trade in lumber, almost all of Malaysia and Brunei, except for the coastal marshes and the highest mountain peaks, was covered by forest. As Wallace described his first view of Sarawak's interior in the 1850's, "For hundreds of miles in every direction a magnificent forest extended over plain and mountain, rock and morass. . . ."

Malaysia still has vast expanses of forest, especially in northern Borneo, though much of it has been lost to logging. Spurred by an insatiable appetite for wood in the international market, and especially in Japan, the pace of logging has accelerated in recent years, despite pressure from international and domestic environmental organizations and an emerging forest-protection movement among Iban and other native peoples of Borneo. An estimated one third of all of northern Borneo's forest was cut down for timber in the 1980's alone, and much of the logging has been done in the form of clear-cutting—every single tree in a given area is cut down, leaving only bare earth behind.

A closer look at what at first glance seems to be virgin forest also reveals clearings on a smaller scale, where patches of forest have been cut down by traditional swidden farmers to create fields for vegetables, rice, or, in Sarawak, small pepper plantations. These fields are used for a few years until the soil declines in fertility, at which time they are abandoned to reseed themselves with second-growth forest. From the air, or across a valley, such second-growth patches show up as areas of smaller, younger trees amidst the tall canopy of the uncut forest.

Iban longboats tied up at a gravel bar on the Skrang River, in the heart of Sarawak's rain forest.

The rain forest of Malaysia, like rain forests everywhere in the tropics, is a storehouse of incredible biological diversity. Soaring but shallowly rooted giant trees rise to form an unbroken canopy, below which lianas, rattan vines, strangler figs, and other trees and vines struggle for a share of light. Canopy trees that are felled by wind or age create small clearings that quickly are filled with new seedlings. Every mature tree is draped with bromeliads, orchids, ferns, and other plants that take root on tree branches far above the forest floor. This plant community is home to an enormous number of animals, including hundreds of species of birds, and smaller numbers of mammals, including several types of deer as well as monkeys, gibbons, and orangutans.

Formerly wild elephants were common in the forests of the Malay Peninsula, and rhinoceroses were found in Borneo. Now the Borneo rhino is apparently extinct, and the number of elephants (along with other large animals such as tigers and wild oxen) on the Peninsula has declined drastically.

The most numerous forest animals, however, are insects: Thousands of species of beetles, hundreds of species of ants, butterflies, and wasps swarm at every level of the forest from the subfloor to the canopy. Wild bees are numerous; in premodern times beeswax was one of Sarawak's principal export commodities. The insects provide food, in turn, for many kinds of amphibians and reptiles, from tiny tree frogs to giant toads. Larger reptiles include monitor lizards capable of hunting and eating deer, giant pythons, and crocodiles.

The Malay Peninsula's finest stands of virgin forest are preserved in the Taman Negara (National Park), covering 1,676 square miles (4,343 square kilometers) in the highlands of Kelantan, Terengganu, and Pahang. This magnificent park has preserved from the ravages of the loggers a huge forest in all of its botanical and zoological diversity; it is home also for some of West Malaysia's 100,000 *orang asli*, or aborigines—tribal peoples driven into the deep forests and high mountains by the spreading waves of Malay migrants to the Peninsula several thousand years ago.

Other large national parks preserve forest tracts in Sarawak and Sabah; in Brunei, the cutting of virgin forest is entirely prohibited. In one of the most promising developments in recent years for the preservation of the Borneo rain forest, negotiations have begun between the governments of Malaysia and Indonesia for the creation of a large international park in the central mountain range straddling the boundary between Sarawak and Kalimantan. Nevertheless, much of Malaysia's primeval forest has been lost beyond recovery, the land converted to other uses.

The Orangutan

The largest of the Asian great apes, the orangutan is a shy, solitary, tree-dwelling distant cousin of human beings; its name (in Malay, *orang hutan*) means "man of the forest." Orangutans were once widespread in the islands of Southeast Asia, but extensive destruction of their rain-forest habitat has severely reduced their range; as Wallace noted more than a century ago, "a wide extent of unbroken and equally lofty virgin forest is necessary to the comfortable existence of these animals." Few orangutans now exist in the wild outside Borneo and Sumatra.

With short legs and long, powerful arms, orangutans seem awkward on the ground, but in the treetops, where they spend most of their time, they are graceful and well adapted. They are vegetarians, living on a diet of leaves, wild figs, and other forest plants and fruit. Male orangutans can weigh up to 150–170 pounds and, in maturity, develop fierce-looking extended cheeks and jowls; females are considerably smaller and more slender than males. Both sexes are covered by coarse, reddish-brown hair. Orangutans live to about thirty years of age in the wild, and in that time have only

Agriculture

The stereotypical image of Southeast Asian agriculture, with steep valleys covered with terraced fields of emerald-green rice, for the most part does not apply to Malaysia. Malaysia does produce rice, along with vegetables and other food crops; but overwhelmingly, Malaysian agriculture is plantation agriculture. At a distance much of Malaysia seems three or four babies; their low reproductive rate combined with their shrinking habitat has put them in danger of extinction in modern times.

Although both Malaysia and Indonesia have passed laws protecting orangutans, poachers continue to carry on a trade in baby orangutans, which are sold as pets. Because the only way to capture a baby orangutan is to shoot its mother, and because many captured babies die before they can be sold, it has been estimated that five to eight animals are killed for every one that is sold alive. In 1964, the Malaysian government established the Sepilok Orangutan Sanctuary near Sandakan, Sabah, to rescue captured baby orangutans and return them to the forest. The rehabilitation process is long and difficult, because the babies have to be taught to climb trees, find food, and survive on their own—all things that they normally would learn from their mothers. The sanctuary has succeeded in returning over one hundred orangutans to life in the wild. Without continued efforts to safeguard large areas of forest from logging and burning, however, the future of the orangutan will continue to be precarious.

still to be heavily forested, and the observer wonders what all the fuss over deforestation has been about. But a closer look reveals that much of Malaysia's "forest" consists of plantations of rubber and oil-palm trees. Where a true tropical forest supports dozens, or even hundreds, of species of trees in an area of a few square miles, the plantations (or, as the Malaysians usually call them, "estates") that have replaced the forest consist of mile after mile of a single species of carefully tended domesticated trees. In addition to rubber and palm oil, other important Malaysian agricultural crops are also produced on plantations, including pineapples in West Malaysia and, in the highlands there, tea; and pepper in Sarawak.

Rubber, which became an important industrial commodity in the nineteenth century (especially with the invention of the pneumatic rubber tire at the dawn of the automobile age), was originally produced primarily in the Amazon Basin of Brazil, the native home of the rubber tree. Malaysia produced only a small amount of a different type of rubber, called gutta-percha, from an unrelated species of rubber tree. But in 1877 some rubber tree seeds were taken from Brazil to England (legend has it that these seeds were "smuggled" out of Brazil, but in fact they were exported legally and openly); seedlings were raised in the

A rice farmer in Sabah sprays his field with insecticides.

English Royal Botanical Gardens. A few years later, rubber tree plantations were established on the Malay Peninsula, and in the early twentieth century the Malay States (as the country was then called) became the world's largest producer of natural rubber. Rubber is now grown in many places in the world's tropical regions, but Malaysia remains a major producer. The Malaysian rubber industry has taken a leading role in breeding new strains of rubber trees that are disease resistant and highly productive.

The establishment of rubber plantations was directly responsible for bringing Indians to Malaya. The vast rubber estates, which were entirely owned by British corporations, needed a supply of cheap labor to perform the difficult work of tapping and processing rubber; they found that labor supply in what is now the southeastern Indian state of Tamil Nadu. Most of Malaysia's Indians are Tamils, and most of them remain rural rubber workers, working on rubber estates (now Malaysian owned) in conditions of hardship and near-poverty.

Rubber is produced by cutting a shallow gash into the bark of the rubber tree, allowing milky liquid latex to run down into a small cup. Cups of latex are collected from tree after tree on the plantation; after the trees have been allowed to rest for a few days, a new groove is cut and latex is collected again. The liquid latex is taken to a processing center, where it is smoked over a fire and formed into solid sheets of rubber. With different kinds of additional processing, the rubber can be made into products ranging from surgical gloves to tractor tires.

Palm oil, Malaysia's second-largest plantation crop, is produced from the fruit of the oil-palm tree. Native to Africa, oil-palm trees began to be grown in Malaysia in the 1920's and became an instant success. The area devoted to oil-palm plantations was greatly expanded after World War II. The oil-palm tree produces large, oil-rich fruit. After the fruit is harvested, the rind and kernels are separated. The rind produces an

industrial-grade oil, while the kernels, when crushed, yield an edible oil that can be used to make margarine, cooking oil, and related products. Palm oil is high in saturated fat, and the rise in dietary health consciousness has therefore depressed the export market for palm oil to the United States and Western Europe. But because palm oil is also relatively inexpensive, it remains in common use in the less-developed countries of the world.

Harvesting the fruit of the oil-palm tree is rough and difficult work, involving climbing a ladder to reach the fruit amidst the stiff palm fronds that surround it; it is dangerous work as well, for the underbrush in oil-palm plantations is an ideal habitat for many of Malaysia's poisonous snakes. Oil-palm plantations, too, rely on cheap labor; much of the work—especially in Sabah, but on the Peninsula as well—is done by Indonesian immigrants.

Sarawak is the world's largest producer of black pepper, and the quest for pepper—which is an effective preservative for meat, and which adds savor to almost any food—was an important spur to Europe's Age of Expansion, beginning in the fifteenth century. Pepper grows on a vine, which, when cultivated as a plantation crop, is trained on a wooden framework some eight to ten feet tall. The vine produces clusters of berries, green at first but ripening to bright red; the berries are picked and sun dried to form peppercorns. Small pepper plantations, planted in forest clearings, are a staple of Iban economic life. Every Iban longhouse is built with a wide bamboo verandah on which woven palm-leaf mats may be spread for use in drying peppercorns.

Although they have the same name in English, the pepper vine is completely unrelated to the bell pepper, the chili pepper, and other members of the capsicum family. Those "vegetable" peppers are native

A rubber tree on a West Malaysia plantation shows the parallel grooves cut into its bark to allow liquid latex to flow into a small cup for collection.

· 41 ·

to Central America; they were brought to Asia by the Spanish, via their colony in the Philippines. Just as black pepper from Sarawak is today a key spice in cuisines around the world, capsicum peppers—the hotter the better—are now an important ingredient in Malay cooking.

Also prominent in Malaysian agriculture, and the Malaysian diet, are many varieties of tropical fruit. Some are familiar in markets around the world, including pineapples, mangoes, and bananas (but a Malaysian market will have a dozen varieties of banana, instead of just one or two). Others are eaten only locally; these include the rambutan (a close relative of the lychee, but with a hairy, rather than a leathery, rind), and the mangosteen, the small pearly-white fruit segments of which are hidden inside a thick, purplish-brown rind. Incredibly delicious, the mangosteen is unknown outside the Asian tropics because it cannot survive being shipped long distances; it spoils within a few hours of being picked. But the king of Malaysian fruit is the durian, which smells foul but tastes wonderful. The fruit of a tree, the durian is the size and shape of a football covered with sharp thorns; it has a thick skin that protects its soft, custardlike flesh. In a famous passage in his great work *The Malay Archipelago*, Alfred Russel Wallace described his encounter with the durian:

The banks of the Sarawak River are everywhere covered with fruit trees, which supply the Dyaks with a great deal of their food. The Mangosteen, Lansat, Rambutan, Jack, Jambou, and Blimbing, are all abundant; but most abundant and most esteemed is the Durian, a fruit about which very little is known in England, but which both by natives and Europeans in the Malay Archipelago is reckoned superior to all others. The old traveller Linschott, writing in 1599, says: "It is of such an excellent taste that it surpasses in flavour all the other fruits of the world, according to those who have tasted it." And Doctor Paludanus adds: "This fruit is of a hot and humid nature. To those not used to it, it seems at first to smell like rotten onions, but immediately they have tasted it they prefer it to all other food. The natives give it honorable titles, exalt it, and make verses on it." When brought into a house the smell is often so offensive that some persons can never bear to taste it. This was my own case when I first tried it in Malacca, but in Borneo I found a ripe fruit on the ground, and, eating it out of doors, I at once became a confirmed Durian eater. . . . In fact to eat Durians is a new sensation, worth a voyage to the East to experience.

The Land: Human Transformations

In an important sense, the nation of Malaysia is a creation of its coastline, which is very long in proportion to the nation's total land area. The country's access to the sea, and especially its location next to the strategic Strait of Malacca, placed it at the crossroads of Asian maritime trade. Malaysia's industries, cities, and transport systems all derive from its position as a nation open to the sea.

The Coast

Malaysia's very long coastline can be thought of as being divided into four sections, each with quite different characteristics.

The west coast of the Malay Peninsula forms the eastern shore of the

Strait of Malacca. Because the narrow and sheltered waterway lacks both heavy surf and high tides, the water meets the land placidly; in some places, farmland reaches down to the very edge of the sea, while in others, mangrove swamps, mud flats, and sandbars at river mouths blur the boundary between land and water. There are only a few sandy beaches on this coast. The coastline is dotted with towns and cities; most were formerly busy ports, but are now rather sleepy and even somewhat run-down, because modern trade has moved to newer facilities such as those at Port Klang. The island of Penang lies off the Peninsula's northwestern coast.

Fishing boats tied up near their owners' houses at Marang, a village on the east coast of the Malay Peninsula.

Traditional shipwrights building a sailing ship, Kuala Terengganu. The ship's keel and sternpost are massive timbers cut from solid teak logs; teak planking is shaped and fitted using only hand tools and wooden nails.

The east coast of the Malay Peninsula, in contrast, faces the open waters of the South China Sea, and is fringed by sandy beaches for most of its length. Cities and towns cluster at the mouths of the coast's many rivers, the harbors filled with small fishing boats. Some of these towns, most notably Kuala Terengganu, are centers of traditional boat building. The coast near Rantau Abang is famous as a breeding ground of giant sea turtles, which come ashore at night to lay their eggs. Off the coast are occasional coral-fringed islands, some of which have recently been developed as resorts for weekend visitors from Kuala Lumpur and Singapore. The largest and best known of these islands, Pulau Tioman, is the very image of what a tropical island should be—so much so that it was used for on-location filming of the movie *South Pacific*.

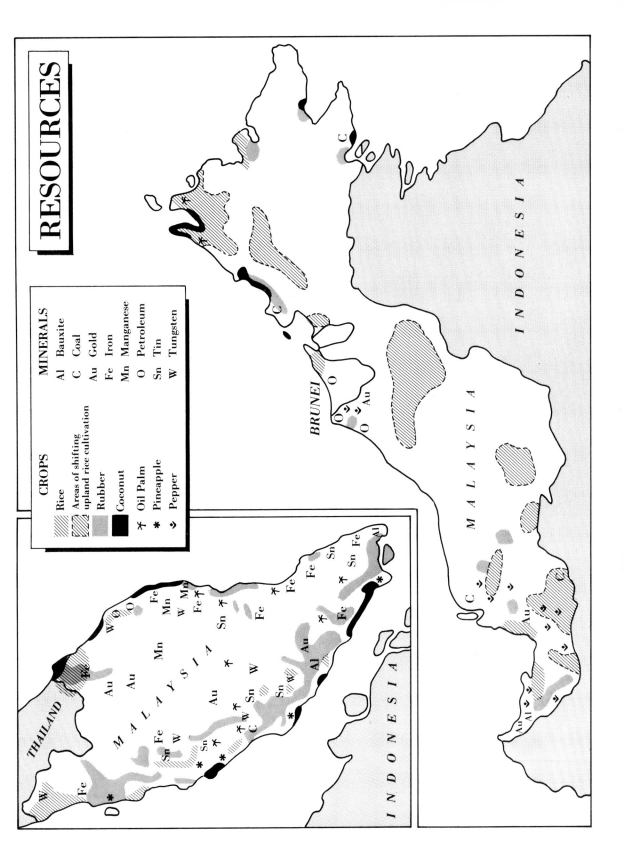

RESOURCES

CROPS

Rice	▨
Areas of shifting upland rice cultivation	▨
Rubber	▨
Coconut	■
Oil Palm	⋎
Pineapple	✳
Pepper	⤸

MINERALS

Al	Bauxite	Mn	Manganese
C	Coal	O	Petroleum
Au	Gold	Sn	Tin
Fe	Iron	W	Tungsten

THAILAND

MALAYSIA

INDONESIA

BRUNEI

MALAYSIA

INDONESIA

The coast of Sarawak (and Brunei as well) is primarily a vast stretch of mangrove swamps; it has few sandy beaches. One interesting effect of this swampy coastline is that there are almost no towns on the ocean itself. Instead, the old port towns, such as Kuching and Bandar Seri Begawan, were built several miles upstream from the coast along the great rivers of northern Borneo, in places where a bend in the river provided deep water and a good anchorage. The two truly coastal cities of Sarawak, Bintulu and Miri, are modern exceptions to the rule. Bintulu is a center for the production of offshore natural gas, and Miri (just west of Brunei) produces both natural gas and crude oil from offshore wells.

The Niah Caves

Some of the world's most spectacular caves are found near Miri, Sarawak, where over a period of millions of years water seeped into the porous limestone hills of the region, dissolving the rock to form caverns. The most famous of Sarawak's caves are at Niah National Park; at some places in the extensive network of caverns there, the cave ceiling looms several hundred feet above the floor.

The Niah caves are home to millions of bats and swiftlets (a kind of insect-eating bird), which deposit many tons of droppings (guano) on the cave floor every year. The guano deposits are mined and sold as fertilizer. The Niah swiftlets build unique nests, made from the birds' congealed saliva, on the cave walls; those nests are the key ingredient in the famous Chinese delicacy birds'-nest soup. Because of their high value—as much as $300 per pound—the nests are collected and sold. Nest collecting is daring and

The coast of Sabah also includes many miles of mangrove swamp, but the terrain of some areas has produced extensive sandy beaches as well, many of which are protected by offshore coral islands. The beach near Kota Kinabalu, the state's capital, stretches for many miles. A small portion has been developed as a luxury resort, but most of it is nearly deserted, except for exercise boys from the local racetrack, who gallop their horses on the beach and cool them down in the surf. West of Kota Kinabalu, near the eastern border of Brunei, lies the island of Labuan, which is large enough to support a port town, an airport, and some industry.

At Kudat, on the northeastern tip of Sabah, the South China Sea

dangerous; collectors, who pass down the techniques of their trade from generation to generation, climb towering bamboo ladders or lower themselves on ropes from narrow platforms high on the cave walls to reach the nests.

In the 1950's, archaeologists excavating a portion of the caves found a human skull 40,000 years old buried under sixteen feet (five meters) of guano, spectacular proof of the antiquity of human occupation of Borneo. In another portion of the Niah cave system, known as the Painted Cave, rock paintings depicting "ships of the dead" and other rituals of local longhouse peoples date back to around A.D. 700. Other archaeological evidence indicates that even at that early time, the Niah Cave People collected birds' nests, as well as other exotic products such as hornbill ivory, and traded them to Chinese merchants for porcelain, metal tools, and other manufactured goods.

meets the Sulu Sea; the boundary between Malaysia and the Philippines lies just off the coast to the east. Southward along Sabah's east coast, coral reefs protect much of the coastline, and small coral islands lie offshore. The Turtle Islands, near the city of Sandakan, are, like the east coast of the Peninsula, a breeding ground for sea turtles. Some of the islands in this group are part of the Philippines. Not far from the coast, south of Sandakan, the Gomantong Caves are the nesting place for thousands of swiftlets; as at the more famous Niah Caves of Sarawak, the birds' edible nests are collected for export. At Semporna, in Sabah's extreme southeast, are hundreds of tiny coral islands and reefs teeming with tropical fish; the area is rapidly becoming known internationally as a diver's paradise.

Mining and Petroleum

Malayan tin was exported through the trade routes of Southeast Asia for many centuries before the coming of the Europeans, but it was not until the nineteenth century that tin mining began to dominate the Malayan economy, and Malaya became one of the world's leading suppliers of tin. Malaysia's tin deposits are concentrated in the western part of the Malay Peninsula, principally in the state of Perak. Tin mining was responsible for much of Malaysia's large Chinese population, as thousands of Chinese "coolie" laborers were imported by British mine owners to do the heavy work of dredging and sifting gravel laced with particles of tin. Some Chinese workers went on to become independent prospectors, and a few became wealthy by owning large mines. A large portion of Malaysia's tin production continues to be done through small

A tin dredge working in a pond north of Kuala Lumpur. Most tin mining in Malaysia is done in small-scale operations like this one, dredging tin-bearing gravel from deposits in old river beds. Popperfoto

dredging operations, almost all Chinese owned. Tin dredging is extremely destructive to the land, leaving behind extensive scars on the landscape and large piles of discarded dirt; much of Perak looks ravaged and desolate from decades of mining. The tin deposits have now become somewhat depleted, and tin is decreasing in importance in Malaysia's economy, both relatively and absolutely.

In economic value, tin has been completely eclipsed by oil and natural gas. Petroleum was discovered in Brunei in 1929; the Brunei Shell Corporation was formed to drill for oil (both onshore and, later, offshore) under license from the sultans of Brunei. Oil revenues rapidly transformed Brunei's ruling dynasty from a minor house of obscure sultans to one of the world's richest families. In the 1970's new oil and natural-gas fields were discovered in Sarawak and Sabah, near Brunei, and oil and gas exports began to play a growing role in Malaysia's economy. The discovery in the early 1980's of an even larger offshore oil and gas field in Terengganu, on the east coast of the Malay Peninsula, has accelerated Malaysia's development as a major exporter of oil and liquefied natural gas.

Malaysia's other mineral resources include iron ore in the Malay Peninsula, coal (though of relatively poor quality) in Sarawak and Sabah, gold in Sarawak and the northern Malay Peninsula, antimony in Sarawak, and bauxite (aluminum ore) in Sabah. Coal mining was commercially important in Sarawak in the nineteenth century, but has since declined into insignificance. Sarawak also produces small quantities of gemstones.

Cities

The cities of Malaysia are often thought of as being either "old" or "new" cities, but Malaysia has no cities that are really very old. Before the coming of the Europeans, Peninsular Malaya was essentially rural. Foreign trade was carried on through a handful of ports, only one of which, Melaka, was large enough to call a city. The sultans of the country's various small states had their capitals in towns that were dominated by palaces and mosques, but had little commerce and industry. Most people lived in agricultural *kampungs* and had little contact with either town dwellers or foreign merchants. At the same time, northern Borneo was almost entirely a land of forest settlements of native peoples, with scarcely any towns, let alone cities.

Malaysia's oldest city is Melaka (formerly spelled Malacca), ideally situated to take advantage of the trade route of the Strait of Malacca. Writing in 1599, Captain Lindschott described Melaka as a trading center responsible for the spread of the Malay language throughout the East Indies:

This place is the market of all India, of China, of the Moluccas, and of other islands round about, from all which places . . . arrive ships, which come and go incessantly, charged with an infinity of merchandises. . . . The origin of this town, as the natives say, was very small, only having at the beginning, by reason of the unhealthiness of the air, but six or seven fishermen who inhabited it. But the number was increased by the meeting of fishermen from Siam, Pegu, and Bengal, who came and built a city. . . . The name of Malacca was given to this town, which, by the convenience of its situation, in a short time grew to such wealth, that it does not yield to the most powerful towns and regions round about. . . . Their language is in vogue throughout the Indies, as the French is here.

Most international trade is now handled through other ports, and Melaka's small river port is used only by local coastal shipping. The town retains much of the flavor of its long history, with a Portuguese fort and church, a foreigners' cemetery, a Dutch church and administrative buildings, and other evidence of colonial rule. But the real spirit of Melaka is Chinese. Most of Melaka's population is Chinese, many of them "Straits Chinese" whose ancestors arrived there a century or more ago. Their distinctive houses (many of them quite grand, the product of wealth earned from tin mines, rubber plantations, and international trade) line the streets of the old town near the river mouth. Melaka has become a favorite destination of foreign visitors seeking a sense of Malaysia's historical past.

George Town, on the island of Penang, is also an old city, founded at the end of the eighteenth century and used as the center of British colonial rule for much of the next century and a half. Like Melaka, George Town is primarily a Chinese city, but it has a large district filled with the handsome houses, churches, and administrative buildings of the British colonialists.

Kuching, the capital of Sarawak, also counts as one of Malaysia's "old" cities, though prior to the 1840's it was a mere village. The capital of the Brooke Dynasty of independent British rulers of Sarawak, it boasts a handsome fort, a small palace, and an excellent museum, as well as other buildings from the colonial era. The old downtown of Kuching is primarily a Chinese city, but it is now ringed by new suburbs and industrial districts of Malays, Iban, and Melanaus, aided by government policies designed to advance the economic status of *bumiputras*.

The cities of the Peninsula's east coast present an interesting contrast with those of the west coast. Whereas the latter are older and heavily Chinese, the east-coast cities are newer and predominantly Malay. Major east-coast cities like Kota Baru, Kuala Terengganu, and Kuantan originated as administrative towns of Malay sultanates. Though each has a small commercial Chinatown, the real focus of these cities is the palace and the mosque.

Kuala Lumpur, Malaysia's capital, is both an old and a new city. Again, "old" here means not very old. The city did not exist until the 1860's, when Chinese tin prospectors found tin-bearing gravel in the

George Town, on Penang Island, West Malaysia, is famous for its stately old government buildings, built during the heyday of British colonialism in the nineteenth century.

"muddy river junction" that gave the city its name. Prosperity from tin mining made the city grow rapidly, with a predominantly Chinese population and an English ruling class. By the early twentieth century, Kuala Lumpur was a very attractive small city; its railway station, post office, and other public buildings were built in an extravagant Victorian Malay-Moorish style, and its broad green *medan* (parade ground) was dominated by the timbered buildings of the exclusive Selangor Club. The city then changed little until the 1960's, when the newly independent Malaysian government built a strikingly modern National Mosque downtown and the Parliament Building and other administrative buildings in a large park on the city's fringe. The city remained an open, low-rise, and rather slow-paced place until the 1980's, when an eco-

nomic boom created an orgy of new construction. Whole blocks of small Chinese and Indian commercial buildings were demolished to make room for office towers and freeways, and today the *medan* itself is disappearing under encroaching buildings. New office buildings and shopping centers sometimes stand literally next door to squalid slumlike apartment buildings, while shantytowns housing migrants from poor rural areas and illegal immigrants from Indonesia often spring up temporarily on lots cleared for future construction. The city now spreads for miles in every direction, ringed by exclusive residential areas of private mansions and other districts of factories and warehouses.

The boomtown atmosphere of Kuala Lumpur has been repeated in other new cities as well. Johor Baru is still graced by the palace and state mosque of the Sultan of Johor, but the city's proximity to Singapore, the most important international port in Southeast Asia, has led to extensive commercial and industrial development for miles around. The single causeway across the narrow strait separating Johor Baru from Singapore is choked with traffic that backs up in hours-long traffic jams at the Malaysian and Singaporean customs and immigration posts. A recent plan to build a second causeway has sparked a frenzy of land speculation and commercial construction in Johor Baru's western districts.

Kota Kinabalu, once the sleepy colonial town of Jesselton (mostly destroyed during World War II), is another boomtown, its economy fueled by petroleum and natural gas, logging, rubber and palm-oil exports, construction, and tourism. Sandakan, Sabah's other large city, is a major timber port; it has also experienced extensive industrial development during the 1980's.

Downtown Kuala Lumpur is a study in architectural contrasts. But Islamic influences are seen in both old and new buildings, for example in the Malayan-Moorish roof pavilions of the old railway station and the high arches and filigree windows of a new office tower.

Bandar Seri Begawan, the capital of Brunei, is a special case because of the vast oil-based wealth of Brunei's ruling family. Writing in 1926, Frank G. Carpenter described the Sultan of Brunei's capital as

all water and houses. The boats anchor among the rude buildings and the market is made up of stalls, each of which is a canoe. Other canoes move about carrying the purchasers from stall to stall. The sellers are women wearing enormous hats. A new town is growing up on the mainland.

But the discovery of oil in Brunei three years later changed that picture very quickly. Today, many of Bandar Seri Begawan's citizens still live in stilt houses in water villages, but those houses have running water, air conditioning, color television sets, and other modern conveniences; fast motorized water taxis have replaced canoes for transportation. On dry land, a small, Chinese-dominated downtown district (with dozens of stores selling gold jewelry) is surrounded by the sumptuous State Mosque, the sultan's palace—with over 2,000 rooms, the largest palace in the world—an international conference center, an international airport, and other symbols of an extremely wealthy modernity.

Most of Brunei's urbanized population is concentrated in and around Bandar Seri Begawan; the country's other major population center is around the towns of Kota Belait and Seria, near the coastal oilfields in the northwest.

Transportation and Communications

The Malay Peninsula is served by a trunk railway that runs north from Singapore all the way to Chiang Mai in northern Thailand. In Malaysia the railroad has two branches, one in the west connecting Johor Baru with Kuala Lumpur, Ipoh, Butterworth (on the mainland opposite Penang), and Alor Setar, and the other running through the central high-

Water taxis are an important mode of transportation in Bandar Seri Begawan, Brunei. About 25,000 of the city's residents still live in stilt houses in kampung air, *or water villages, like the one in the background.*

lands to Kota Baru on the east coast. The two branches rejoin in southern Thailand. There are no railroads anywhere on Borneo.

An energetic highway building program has created excellent roads along the western and eastern coasts of the Peninsula, and many branch highways among the cities of the west coast. But the Peninsula's mountainous terrain still hinders communications, and there are only three highways connecting the east and west coasts in all of Peninsular Malaysia. A coastal highway in Sarawak was completed only in the late 1980's, making it possible for the first time to cross the entire state overland. Widespread logging has led to the creation of an extensive network of rough dirt roads suitable for logging trucks, but except on the coastal highway, overland travel in Sarawak still ranges from difficult to impossible. Most local traffic still relies more on riverboats and motorized canoes than on cars and trucks. Sabah has a good highway that runs along the north coast and then crosses the central mountain range, connecting Kota Kinabalu with Sandakan, but there are few other roads in the interior. Wealthy Brunei has a small but excellent highway system in the vicinity of the capital.

Long-distance travel in Malaysia depends heavily on the country's extensive air-transport network. Trunk routes and small feeder flights serve all of Malaysia's major cities and many smaller towns.

As a rapidly industrializing country, Malaysia has a modern and well-developed telecommunications system, with television, radio, and telephone service available in all but the most remote areas. Brunei is, of course, similarly well served.

Malaysia is and will remain a country of tremendous geographical, ethnic, and cultural diversity, but modern transportation and communications are playing an increasingly important role in forging a new sense of national unity.

Before the Europeans

The early history of Malaya and northern Borneo is difficult to reconstruct; what little is known must be inferred from a small amount of physical evidence from archaeological sites, as well as from ethnographic and linguistic studies of later peoples of Indonesia and Australasia. Archaeologists and anthropologists do not always agree about how and when various peoples passed through the Malay Peninsula, and whether population shifts took place as relatively sudden, well-defined waves of migration or as slower spreads of populations over longer periods of time. But we do know that the Malay Peninsula served as a highway from mainland Asia to island Southeast Asia for tens of thousands of years.

Among those who made the journey south along the Peninsula and beyond were Australoid and Veddetic peoples, the ancestors of the Aborigines of Australia and the Papuans of New Guinea, beginning over 40,000 years ago. They were followed by Negritos, who later wound up settling in eastern Indonesia, and by Melanesoids, ancestors of the Melanesians of the islands north and east of New Guinea.

The long-distance migrations of these peoples were not quite so difficult as the present-day map of the East Indies might suggest. During the great Ice Ages that ended around 15,000 years ago, so much of the earth's seawater was locked up in glacial ice that sea levels fell by as much as 330 feet (100 meters). Much of the Sunda Shelf (the seafloor between Malaya, Sumatra, and Java) and the Arafura Sea (between New Guinea and Australia) was dry land at the time. Migrants through what are now peninsulas and islands would have had to cross only narrow stretches of open water, not wide seas. The migrations were probably slow and gradual, taking place over many generations. Still, these ancient population movements provide striking evidence of the powerful urge to explore new territory that seems built into human consciousness.

The ancestors of the Malays were relative latecomers to the Peninsula, which had been traversed and settled many times before. According to one widely accepted historical theory, people who spoke one or another language ancestral to those in the Malayan language group arrived in the Peninsula in two distinct waves. Historians refer to the peoples of these two waves as Proto-Malays (earliest Malays) and Deutero-Malays (second Malays).

The Proto-Malays came in a series of small migrations over a long period of time, between about 7,000 and 4,500 years ago. Originating somewhere in Vietnam, they were crowded out of their homeland by expanding populations of other peoples in South China and northern Vietnam, Laos, and Thailand, and began to move south. They brought

Time Line: Malaya and Brunei from Earliest Times to 1815

5000–2500 B.C.   Migrations of Proto-Malays to Malay Peninsula and adjacent islands

500–100 B.C.   Migrations of Deutero-Malays to Malay Peninsula and adjacent islands; Proto-Malays absorbed or driven to marginal areas

100 B.C.   Beginning of occasional maritime trade between Han Dynasty China and Roman Empire

A.D. 400   Indian merchants in Sumatra and Malay Peninsula; earliest trading kingdoms founded

7TH CENT.   Srivijaya founded in Sumatra

8TH CENT.   Sailendra founded in Java; Borobudur built, ca. 778–824

CA. 850   Fall of Sailendra, rise of Mataram

CA. 900   Temple of Prambanan built

1006   Srivijaya defeats Mataram

1026–45   Srivijaya defeated and occupied by Indian Chola Empire

1042   Death of King Airlangga; Mataram divided into Janggala and Kediri

1222   Fall of Kediri

CA. 1380–1420   Strong Thai cultural influence in Malay Peninsula

1290   Fall of Srivijaya

1292   Mongol invasion of Java; Majapahit Empire founded

CA. 1400   Rise of Ayuthaya Empire in Thailand

1402   Melaka founded

1456–1498   Tun Perak as Prime Minister of Melaka

LATE 14TH–EARLY 15TH CENT.   Brunei controls northern Borneo and southern Philippines under Sultan Bolkiah V

1511   Portuguese conquer Melaka

1600   British East India Company founded

1602   Dutch East India Company founded

1623   Ambon massacre; British driven from Spice Islands

1641   Dutch conquer Melaka

1782   Fall of Ayuthaya; Kingdom of Siam founded

1786   Penang ceded to British by Sultan of Kedah

LATE 18TH CENT.   Rise of British opium trade from India to China

1811–15   British occupy Melaka and Java; Raffles serves as governor of Java

with them a relatively advanced "stone age" culture, making extensive use of bamboo and plant fibers for shelter, tools, and clothing, and practicing a mixed economy of hunting, food gathering, and cultivation of tubers, vegetables, and other crops. They had no knowledge of metal, and almost certainly had no large-scale social or political organization; they lived in small villages or led seminomadic lives in the forest. Nevertheless, they were more numerous and powerful than the people they found already living in the Peninsula, and those people were driven out, absorbed, or forced into a marginal existence in the most remote and least promising parts of the mountains and forests.

The Proto-Malays were also skilled in the use of boats, probably small outrigger vessels that could be either paddled or sailed. Using their seafaring skills, they rapidly settled the western islands of Indonesia, from Sumatra to Borneo and Sulawesi. Populations of Proto-Malays in the islands were relatively isolated from each other, and quickly developed into separate ethnolinguistic groups.

The Deutero-Malays

The Deutero-Malays were originally descended from the same stock as the Proto-Malays; they stayed behind in Vietnam when the Proto-Malays departed. In their original homeland, in distant contact with the rice-growing, bronze-making civilizations to their north, they developed a bronze-age agricultural civilization. But the expansion of the Chinese empire into and beyond the Yangtze River Valley from around 500 B.C. to 100 B.C. impelled large numbers of Tai, Mon-Khmer, and Viet people to migrate from South China into Southeast Asia; they in turn crowded out the Deutero-Malays and forced them to migrate south as well.

In a repetition of the familiar pattern, the Deutero-Malays absorbed or pushed out the Proto-Malays whom they found already living on the Peninsula and on Sumatra and Java, and this of course set off still further waves of population movement throughout the islands. The effect of all these migrations was to create in Malaya and western Indonesia a "Greater Malay World," occupied by two distinct types of

Bamboo and Southeast Asian Civilization

Archaeology has been defined as the study of "the stories told by stones." That explains, to some extent, why so little is known about the ancient peoples of Southeast Asia, for they left behind very few stones for archaeologists to study. For many years, the lack of evidence for "stone age" people in Southeast Asia led scholars to suppose that in prehistoric times the region was unpopulated or only very sparsely populated, and that ancient Bronze Age civilizations such as the Dongson Culture of northern Vietnam must have been the creation of immigrants from other regions.

Recently, however, archaeologists have begun to realize that evidence for ancient peoples in Southeast Asia is lacking not because the people were not there, but because they employed mainly perishable materials in making almost everything they used in their daily lives. Brick and stone structures, for example, such as those built in the ancient Near East or Central America, simply were not built in Southeast Asia, and so cannot survive to tell us stories today.

The key to human culture in ancient Southeast Asia was undoubtedly the most comprehensively useful and versatile plant on the face of the earth: bamboo. Even today, in the age of plastics, bamboo is used so widely in Asian cultures that life without it would be almost unthinkable. In very ancient times, when plastic and even metal were not yet available, bamboo was able to provide almost everything that people needed to live comfortable and productive lives. A better name for the "stone age" in Southeast Asia would be the "bamboo age."

The many species of bamboo are among the largest members of the grass family. Some species have hard, dense stems and grow only a few feet tall, others have narrow-walled hollow stems and reach heights of over sixty feet. Bamboo grows abundantly and rapidly—some types can grow over a foot a day—and therefore it is a renewable and readily available resource. Employing only simple stone choppers and scrapers, ancient Southeast Asian people could cut and fashion bamboo in a great many ways.

Bamboo poles and rafters formed the framework for a house; woven split-bamboo mats served as its walls, while palm-leaf thatch laid on bamboo roof poles completed the structure. If a house rotted and fell down after a number of years, a replacement could be made in a few days. A length of dried and fire-hardened bamboo could be shaved into a deadly arrow or spear; a sliver split from the skin of a dried bamboo stem made a razor-sharp, disposable knife. A single section cut from a large bamboo stem (some species have stems over eight inches in diameter) made a bucket for carrying liquids. A similar section split lengthwise made a disposable bowl for serving food.

Because its stems are made of long parallel fibers, bamboo can be split into long pieces as fine and pliable as thread; split bamboo was used to weave everything from body armor to pack baskets to floor mats. A handful of rice boiled inside a tightly woven bamboo-leaf pouch produced a prepackaged dumpling of sticky rice—the ancient Southeast Asian equivalent of take-out food. Bamboo is even edible; young tender bamboo shoots make an excellent vegetable.

The list of bamboo's uses is nearly endless, as anyone who has strolled through an outdoor market anywhere in Southeast Asia can testify. Although nearly all the physical evidence for "bamboo age" culture has perished over the course of time, the central role played by bamboo in Southeast Asia today allows us to make informed guesses about how people must have lived in the same region thousands of years ago.

people: the settled, agricultural, village-dwelling Deutero-Malays, and the tribal, forest-dwelling Proto-Malays. The former are today's Malays (and their close relatives in Sumatra, Java, and Bali); the latter are the various *orang asli* (original peoples) of the Malay world, including the Iban of Borneo, the Toraja of Sulawesi, and many others.

By the time the Malay world was thoroughly settled by Deutero-Malays, they had already developed a distinctive culture of their own. For example, three key features of Malay culture—the *wayang* shadow-puppet theater; music featuring *gamelan* orchestras of drums, xylophones, and flutes; and *batik* and *ikat* resist-dyed textiles (all of which are described in detail in Chapters VII and VIII)—were in evidence during that early period. At the same time, the Malay world shared aspects of culture familiar throughout Southeast Asia.

Long-Distance Trade

The early Malay world was one of agricultural villages, in which people formed cooperative associations to control the irrigation water necessary for the cultivation of rice. Villages were linked by networks of trade, kinship, rivalry, and defense, forming small-scale kingdoms ruled by aristocrats who collected taxes and justified their domination by performing various services. Those included defense, the conduct of important religious ceremonies, rice milling and other agricultural services, the patronage of artists and artisans, and the management of trade. At least along the west coast of the Peninsula, the east coast of Sumatra, and the northern coasts of Java and Borneo, trade soon became the chief activity of these small kingdoms, because trading ships from distant lands were already passing by.

Long-distance sea-trade routes in the Indian Ocean were already well established at the time of the Roman Empire, and routes from China to the South China Sea were in use not long thereafter. The Malay Peninsula itself was known to the Greek geographer Ptolemy in the mid-second century A.D.; he called it the Golden Khersonese. Beginning no later than around A.D. 500, ships from the Red Sea and the Persian Gulf regularly sailed to the Strait of Malacca to buy spices (such as black pepper, cloves, cinnamon, and nutmeg), tin, aromatic sandalwood, and two Chinese products, silk and porcelain. Those were brought from China to trading centers of the Malay world in either Malay, Arab, or Chinese vessels and exchanged for products in high demand in China: pepper, sandalwood, and such exotic goods as hornbill "ivory" (that is, the thick beaks of hornbill birds, used for decorative carving), rhinoceros horn, edible birds' nests, and dried *bêche-de-mer* (known in English by the unappetizing name sea slugs). Little is known about the development of local trade within the Malay world. Presumably goods in demand for world trade were collected by local merchants who would, for example, exchange Chinese goods with the Iban and other tribes in Borneo for hornbill ivory or beeswax and bring those products to centers of long-distance trade along the Strait of Malacca.

Although merchants from many nations came to the Malay world, the most numerous were those from the closest large trading regions, the Malabar Coast of southwestern India and the Coromandel Coast of southeastern India. Because Indian civilization was at that time much more highly advanced than that of the Malay world, the Malays soon began to be strongly influenced by the Indians. The seasonal nature of trade in Malaya enhanced that influence.

Maritime trade in the Indian Ocean was dependent on the monsoon winds, which blow from the southwest from May to September, and from the northeast from December through February. Merchants from India would arrive in the Strait of Malacca in the summer, conduct their business, and then be forced to wait several months until favorable

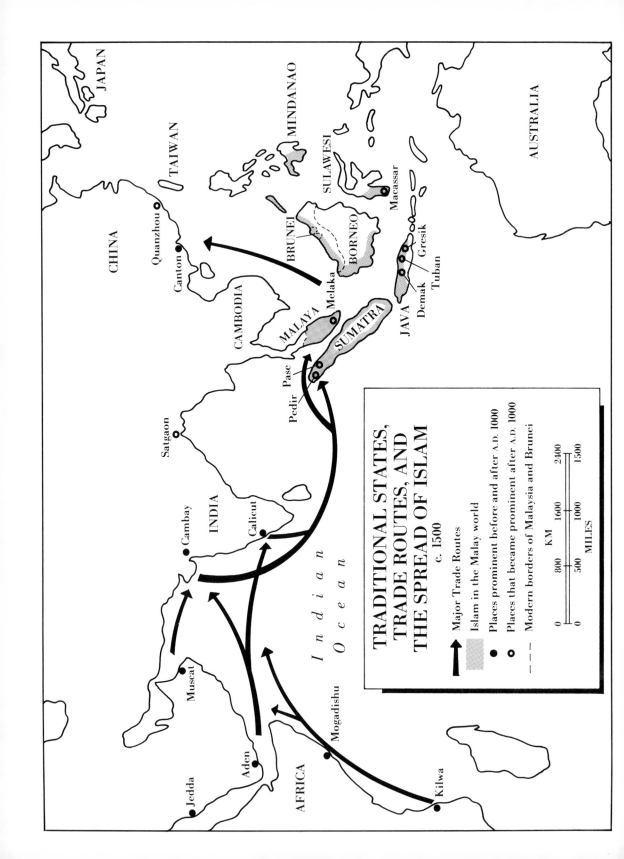

**TRADITIONAL STATES,
TRADE ROUTES, AND
THE SPREAD OF ISLAM**

c. 1500

Major Trade Routes

Islam in the Malay world

Places prominent before and after A.D. 1000

Places that became prominent after A.D. 1000

Modern borders of Malaysia and Brunei

KM
0   800   1600   2400

MILES
0   500   1000   1500

winds would allow their return home. (Conversely, trade from China flowed south in the winter and north in the summer.) Because Indian merchants and sailors had to live in towns along the Malayan coasts for as much as half of every year, permanent colonies of Indians soon sprang up in those towns to provide them with familiar food, lodging, and other comforts of home. Buddhist and Hindu temples were established to serve their religious needs, and Buddhist monks and Hindu Brahmin priests arrived to staff those temples. Local Malay rulers soon found that the skills of those religious leaders were useful to them as well; they looked to them to provide written records (for the Malays at that time had no written language of their own), scientific, technical, and

A Javanese outrigger sailing ship, of a type that would have engaged in trade in the Strait of Malacca during the period of Hindu influence, depicted on the Temple of Borobudur.

astrological advice, and other services. Many members of the Malay elite converted to Buddhism or Hinduism, and so those religions, and the Indian culture associated with them, soon spread rapidly in the Malay world. The Malays (like the Burmese and Khmers farther north) soon became strongly Indianized. (See *The Land and People of Cambodia.*) But when Indianized empires arose in the Malay world, the main action was not in present-day Malaysia, but rather in the nearby islands of Sumatra and Java.

The Early Empires

The first great empire of the Malay world was Srivijaya, which founded its capital at Palembang in southeastern Sumatra in the seventh century A.D. Culturally, Srivijaya was strongly influenced by India. Buddhism was promoted by the rulers of the empire; the Chinese Buddhist monk Yi Jing, who stayed in Palembang both on his way to India on pilgrimage and on his return, reported in A.D. 671 that the city's monasteries held over a thousand monks. Palembang was a great center of long-distance trade; during a period of six months there, Yi Jing recorded the arrival of thirty-five ships from Persia alone. At its height, the Srivijayan Empire controlled all of the Malay Peninsula northward to what is now Burma and Thailand, all of Sumatra, the western third of Java, and the western tip of Borneo, and made energetic efforts to control all trade in the region. Writing in 1225, near the end of the Srivijayan period, another Chinese, Zhao Rugua, said that in former times the rulers of the empire had stretched an iron chain across the Strait of Malacca from Sumatra to Malaya (presumably the chain was buoyed up with logs or even barges) in order to regulate the movement of merchant ships through the strait.

A constant aim of the rulers of Srivijaya, and of all later maritime empires in the region as well, was the suppression of piracy, which for many centuries was—and indeed, remains—an unpleasant fact of life in East Indian waters. Operating in fast ships out of small ports, pirates could easily ambush merchant ships in the confined waters of the Indies, and quickly disappear again into the twisting river channels of their home bases. Efforts to control or eliminate piracy were important to the maritime empires, because safe sea-lanes were more attractive to foreign traders and thus brought more wealth to the empires themselves.

The Strait of Malacca is the best route between the Indian Ocean and the South China Sea, but it is not the only one. The Sunda Strait between Sumatra and Java is also a feasible route, though it requires a longer voyage and is more vulnerable to storms. Another option was to sail from India to the western coast of the Isthmus of Kra (the narrowest part of the Malay Peninsula), unload cargo there, transport it overland to the east coast, and continue on by ship again. Other empires soon arose to challenge the Srivijayan monopoly of power in the region, based in part on access to these alternative trade routes.

In the eighth century, aristocratic refugees from the old kingdom of Funan, in southern Vietnam and Cambodia, founded a kingdom called Sailendra in central Java. Quickly growing in wealth and military manpower in the rich ricelands of Java, the kingdom invaded Indochina and briefly ruled extensive territories in what is now Cambodia and Vietnam. Srivijaya controlled the Strait of Malacca, but its hold was less strong over the Sunda Strait, and that provided a trade link between India and Sailendra. Sailendra was a Buddhist kingdom, and it is best remembered today for its grandest monument, the Temple of Borobudur. A small artificial mountain formed of nine sculptured stone terraces, it is one of the most impressive religious structures ever built anywhere in the world.

The ruling family of Sailendra was overthrown in a coup in 832; ironically, a survivor of that family became ruler of Srivijaya in a peaceful change of dynasty in 850. The successor state to Sailendra in central Java was called Mataram. Its rulers embraced Hinduism rather than Buddhism (which thereafter faded to insignificance in the Malay world), and built the great temple of Prambanan not far from Borobudur. Mataram competed energetically with Srivijaya for control of foreign trade. Its geographic position allowed it to gain the lion's share of trade with China, but Srivijaya blocked Mataram's access to the Strait

The temple-mountain of Borobudur, near Yogyakarta, Java, is one of the most impressive Buddhist monuments in the world. It was built around A.D. 800 by the kings of Sailendra, a Javanese rival of the Sumatran Hindu Srivijayan empire. UNESCO photo

The Hindu temple of Prambanan was built not far from Borobudur in the ninth century A.D. *by the kings of Mataram, a trading empire that succeeded Sailendra in ruling central Java and controlling trade routes with China.*

of Malacca. The two kingdoms went to war in 1006, and Mataram was disastrously defeated.

Srivijaya had little time to enjoy its success, because in 1026 it was invaded by a South Indian king, Rajendra Chola, and thoroughly sacked—the only time in history that Indian armies have invaded Southeast Asia. Chola rule of Srivijaya was short-lived, and the empire recovered. It may seem strange that these empires could fall after being defeated by a rival, and then rapidly rise once again. The reason for this lies in the nature of the empires themselves. They were not, like modern nation-states, based on secure control of territory within clearly defined boundaries. Rather they were maritime empires in which small ruling

· 75 ·

classes grew wealthy through their control of sea-lanes and domination of trade. If their forces were defeated in battle, they would decline as other empires encroached on their area of control, but just as quickly a new leader could rally local supporters, build up his military and naval strength, and assert his empire's power once again.

Not long after its defeat by Srivijaya, the power of Mataram was restored by its greatest king, Airlangga. One of Airlangga's sons established a successor state, Kediri, which soon outshone his father's kingdom. By the end of the twelfth century a Chinese writer, Zhou Zhufei, ranked Kediri first among all the maritime empires of Southeast Asia; it controlled eastern Java, Bali, southern Borneo, and Sulawesi, and dominated the spice trade from the Moluccas.

Kediri was overthrown in 1222 by yet another Javanese kingdom, Singhasari, which went on to defeat and extinguish Srivijaya in 1290. For a brief time, both the Strait of Malacca and the Sunda Strait were under the control of a single empire again. But the triumph was short-lived, for Singhasari was shaken by a rebellion in 1292, and then crushed by an invasion from the Mongol Empire of China in the same year. A counterattack expelled the Mongols, but by then Singhasari was in ruins. A new Hindu-Javanese empire, Majapahit, took over. Under its brilliant prime minister (1331–1364) Gajah Mada, the greatest figure in the history of the ancient Malay world, Majapahit conquered and united virtually the entire East Indies, including part of the Malay Peninsula. For almost two centuries, power throughout Southeast Asia was divided between Majapahit and the Thai empire of Ayuthaya.

The rise of Thai power was facilitated by the destruction of the Burmese kingdom of Pagan by the Mongols in 1287. Beginning in that year, the small Thai kingdom of Sukhotai began to extend its territory at the expense of both the Burmese and the Khmers. A later Sukhotai ruler, King Ramadhipati (ruled 1350–1369), founded a new capital at

Ayuthaya, west of present-day Bangkok, and set about consolidating an empire that controlled much of mainland Southeast Asia, just as Majapahit controlled the islands; the empire endured well into the eighteenth century. The new Thai empire of Ayuthaya competed vigorously with Majapahit and its Malay successors for control of the Strait of Malacca and the alternative overland route across the Isthmus of Kra. By 1400, Ayuthaya had established a trading station at Singapore, at the southern tip of the Malay Peninsula; it threatened to take control of maritime traffic through the Strait of Malacca out of Malay hands.

The Rise of Melaka

The city of Melaka was founded in 1402 by a Sumatran prince named Parameswara, who was exiled as a rebel by his father-in-law, the king. He first fled to Singapore, but was driven out by the Thai rulers there. Finally he wound up in the tiny fishing village of Melaka, and used his influence and contacts to establish it as a port for trade. The new port's convenient location and its ruler's enthusiastic promotion of trade (along with his willingness to use force, if necessary, to make ships stop there) soon turned Melaka into the hub of the Malay world, and indeed of all of Asia's maritime trade. A further effect of the rise of Melaka as a trading center was to bring to the Malay Peninsula new Malay-related immigrants from throughout the East Indies: Minangkabau, Achenese, and Batak from Sumatra; Sundanese and Javanese from Java; and Bugis—the greatest long-distance mariners of the Malay world—from Sulawesi.

Melaka's founding came at a particularly fortunate time. In Europe, the social and economic changes that led to the end of the Middle Ages and the rise of the Renaissance had the effect of creating a vast amount of new wealth. That in turn stimulated an increase in the demand for

Two Chinese enameled porcelain plates from the Ming Dynasty (1368–1644), purchased recently in a curio shop in Sarawak. Chinese porcelain factories produced thousands of tons of this inexpensive ware especially for the Southeast Asian export market; it is commonplace in northern Borneo even today.

luxury goods of all kinds, including the silk, spices, porcelain, and other products of Asia. And in China, the founding of the Ming Dynasty in 1368 had also ushered in an era of new prosperity and flourishing overseas trade.

Parameswara even visited China in 1404, and was rewarded by being given an official seal confirming Chinese recognition of his rule in Melaka. That venture was to prove very important, for China had just embarked on the greatest maritime expeditions in its history. Between 1404 and 1433, a series of huge fleets under the command of Grand Admiral Zheng He was sent from China to pursue trade and diplomacy in the South China Sea, the Indian Ocean, and as far as the Arabian Peninsula and the east coast of Africa. The Chinese fleets made Melaka a regular port of call, enhancing both its wealth and its reputation.

Within a few years, Melaka was crowded with ships and merchants from every part of the Old World. Ayuthaya controlled the eastern coast of the Malay Peninsula, but Melaka's rulers blocked the extension of its power into the Strait of Malacca. They also chipped away at Majapahit's power in the western Indies, siphoning off its trade and challenging its control of territory. Soon Ayuthaya's sphere of influence receded into the Gulf of Thailand, Majapahit was in decline, and Melaka was the greatest commercial power in Southeast Asia.

Melaka's merchants filled outbound ships with cargoes of spices, tin, porcelain and silk (both transshipped from China), rice, sandalwood, and other Asian goods, and handled imports of Indian textiles, Venetian glass, Arabian metalwork, and chests of jewels, silver, and gold. Its most significant import, however, was not any material good, but rather a new religion: Islam.

The Coming of Islam

Islam had long been known in East and Southeast Asia by the time Melaka was founded at the beginning of the fifteenth century. There were mosques in virtually every city along the China coast, and in the trading centers of Sumatra and Java, serving communities of resident Arab merchants. The Vietnamese kingdom of Champa had converted to Islam as early as the tenth century. Yet the Malay world remained loyal to Indian Hinduism, taking its lead in cultural and religious matters, as always, from its greatest trading partner. It was not until sizeable numbers of people in India itself became Muslims that the Malay world followed suit. Islam entered Malaya as an Indian, not an Arab, religion.

The upsurge in trade in the Strait of Malacca in the fifteenth century brought increased numbers of Muslim merchants from the Indian state

Islam

Islam, one of the world's major religions, originated in Mecca, in western Arabia, in the early seventh century A.D. A merchant of Mecca named Mohammed began to receive revelations from Allah (God) which, Muslims believe, represent God's final prophetic message to the world. Islam derived in part from the Biblical traditions of Judaism and Christianity but, in Muslim belief, supersedes those religions. The prophecies revealed to Mohammed, believed to be the literal word of God, were collected in 651 into a book known as the Koran; other sacred texts of Islam include the *hadith*, accounts of Mohammed's life and teachings, and the *sharia*, a body of religious law that is binding on all Muslims.

The Koran teaches that God controls the world and all its creatures absolutely and in every detail; the duty of humans therefore is to submit to the will of God freely and totally. The word Islam itself means "submission." Believers are promised eternal life in paradise after death, while all others face damnation.

Islam makes no distinction between secular and religious life, and religious law governs all human affairs. In particular, Muslims are required to adhere to the Five Pillars of Islam:

1. The profession of faith: "There is no God but God, and Mohammed is His prophet."
2. Prayer five times daily, facing the holy city of Mecca.
3. Giving of alms to the poor.
4. Fasting between dawn and darkness during the month of Ramadan.
5. Making a *hajj* (pilgrimage) to Mecca at least once, if it can be done without causing financial hardship to one's family.

Religious law governs relations within the community and the family, notably the status of women: Women are to be respected and their rights protected, but they are required to dress modestly and obey their fathers and husbands.

In A.D. 622 Mohammed was forced by local opposition to his teachings to flee from Mecca to Medina, where he continued to preach and made many converts to Islam. The Muslim calendar takes A.D. 622 as its year 1. Within a few years after Mohammed's death in 632, much of Arabia had been converted to Islam. Islam is a militantly evangelical religion. It divides humankind into the *Dar ol Islam* (world of submission to God) and the *Dar ol Harb* (world at war with God). Jews and Christians, as "People of the Book" (that is, believers in the Bible) have special status in Islam, but Muslims believe it is their duty to expand the *Dar ol Islam* by converting all others to the true faith.

By about A.D. 750, Arab armies had conquered and converted all of the Middle East and North Africa; both the missionary zeal of the Arabs and the appeal of Islam itself were responsible for the religion's rapid success. In subsequent centuries Islam spread farther, to Spain, East Africa, Central Asia, India, and Southeast Asia.

Islam is divided into several sects. The sects do not differ on religious grounds, for all Muslims regard the Koran as the final word of God, but rather on questions of authority within the Muslim community. The two most important sects are Shi'a, found mostly in the Persian-speaking world, and Sunni Islam, prevalent everywhere else; the Sunni sect in general is more diverse and tolerant than Shi'a. A third sect, derived from Shi'a, is the Sufi movement, which stresses personal devotion to God, mysticism, and scholarship as a means of understanding God's universe.

Nearly all Malays are Sunni Muslims; Sufism, which found a strong following in India, has exerted a considerable influence on Sunni beliefs and practices in the Malay world.

of Gujarat to the region. Their wealth, missionary zeal, and willingness to enter into marriage alliances with local rulers led quickly to the establishment of Muslim states in northern Sumatra. These were organized as Islamic sultanates, that is, absolute monarchies governed by Islamic law, in which all land and people belonged to the ruler. The ruler of one such state was willing to marry his daughter to Parameswara's son, Megat (also known as Sikandar Shah), an alliance that promised to increase further the power of Melaka, but he demanded that Megat convert to Islam first. When Megat followed his father to the throne, he converted his entire army—which included many Javanese and Sumatrans—to Islam; they in turn converted their families back home, contributing further to the new religion's rapid spread.

Indian Islam was a far cry from the strict and zealous orthodoxy of the Arab world. Indian Muslims had long since made their own accommodations between Islam and the beliefs, ceremonies, and culture of Hinduism. Their brand of Islam, tolerant and forgiving, was easy for Malays to accept. When Megat, newly converted to Islam, came to the throne of Melaka, for example, his coronation was accompanied by traditional Hindu ceremonies. Not until long afterward would Malay Islam turn to strict orthodoxy. Even today, while Islamic fundamentalism is gaining strength in Malaysia and Sumatra, most Javanese Muslims still retain strong traces of earlier Hindu belief and practice.

Islam spread rapidly throughout the Malay world in the fifteenth century. New Islamic sultanates, nominally loyal to Melaka, arose in western Java and encroached further on the power of Majapahit. By the sixteenth century Majapahit had shrunk to insignificance in central Java; most of its aristocracy fled to Bali rather than convert to Islam (and Bali remains today the last stronghold of Hinduism in the Malay world). Also during the early fifteenth century the ruler of the small Borneo river port of Brunei converted to Islam and declared himself sultan. By the end of that century his descendant, Sultan Bolkiah V, had created an empire that controlled trade and administration throughout northern Borneo (although in practice it exercised little territorial control over the interior of Borneo) and extended to the islands of the southern Philippines around the Sulu Sea.

Meanwhile Melaka flourished as the strongest of all of Southeast Asia's commercial empires. Its rulers adopted both the Hindu title maharaja and the Persian title shah, thereby elevating themselves above the various sultans of the region. Although Muslims, they imposed no religious test on visiting merchants, and they established an administration that encouraged trade with all comers. Trade was regulated by four *shahbendars* (harbormasters) chosen from among the chief merchants of the city's most important foreign communities, i.e. Gujarat, Bengal, Java, and China. Internal administration was in the hands of a *bendahara* (prime minister), who presided over the Council of State. Melaka's greatest *bendahara*, Tun Perak (in office 1458–1496), is regarded by Malays today as a national hero; under his administration, Melaka rose to the peak of its power.

Yet the administration of Tun Perak also created problems for the future, because by the end of his long reign he had consolidated power so thoroughly in the hands of himself and his family that his death created a crisis. As Melaka's ruling families squabbled for succession after Tun Perak's death, an unprecedented new threat was about to burst upon the scene.

The First Europeans

From the point of view of Europe, the immense wealth of the trade with Asia was a source of temptation and jealousy. Virtually all trade from the Strait of Malacca to Europe passed through the hands of Indian and

Arab merchants, and then to the powerful, wealthy city-states of Italy, particularly Venice and Genoa. The desire of rulers in Western Europe to eliminate those middlemen touched off the European Age of Expansion that ultimately was to spread European power and civilization around the globe. Militant Christianity also played a role in the European expansion. Having recently driven the Islamic Moors from the Iberian Peninsula, the triumphant rulers of Spain (and the Portuguese in competition with them) sought to expand the Christian realm, by force if necessary, around the globe.

The first European ruler to explore ways to circumvent the eastern Mediterranean monopoly on Asian trade was Portugal's Prince Henry the Navigator (1394–1460). Pursuing a steady and well-planned policy of exploration and conquest, he sent fleets down the west coast of Africa that established fortified trading posts wherever they could. Those forts then served as bases for further exploration and conquest. Under Henry's successors, the process continued. Bartholomeu Dias rounded the Cape of Good Hope in 1487–88, clearing the way for Portuguese expansion in the Indian Ocean. Vasco da Gama—the first European to sail around Africa and on to India—attacked Calicut, on India's southwestern coast, in 1498. (The westward voyages of Columbus around the same time represented a Spanish attempt to avoid the emerging Portuguese monopoly on trade and conquest in the Indian Ocean.)

The speed and ruthlessness of the Portuguese advance took the Asian trading empires by surprise. The Portuguese, in the words of Vasco da Gama, sought "Christians and spices," but whereas other merchants had been content to buy and sell, and occasionally to preach, the Portuguese came to conquer and control. Sailing in heavily armed ships with cannon that were far superior to the local weaponry used in Africa and Asia, the Portuguese made military force a key tactic in their rapid maritime expansion. Because their ships carried relatively small crews, they tended to shoot first and talk afterward whenever they sailed into a new port of call, making up in surprise and brutality for their disadvantage in numbers. It is no wonder that the rulers of traditional trading empires in the Indian Ocean and Southeast Asia tended to regard the Portuguese, and other Europeans who came after them, as pirates rather than merchants.

Following da Gama's success in Calicut, the Portuguese throne proclaimed the establishment of the Viceroyalty of India. Under the second Viceroy, Alphonso de Albuquerque (ruled 1509–1515), the Portuguese captured Goa (1510) and Hormuz (1515), securing a Portuguese royal monopoly on trade in the Indian Ocean. At the same time, Albuquerque's mighty fleet advanced on Melaka.

A bronze cannon from Borneo, probably made in the Sultanate of Brunei in the sixteenth century A.D. This type of swivel-mounted small-bore cannon could be used both aboard ships and in defense of fortified houses and palaces. Typically cast with beautiful and extravagant decorative details, such cannon were not only weapons, but also articles of high value and prestige. Courtesy of The Sarawak Museum

The Portuguese attacked Melaka twice in 1511, but were driven away not only by the shah's armed forces, but also by the combined fleets of the resident merchants. But a third attack succeeded. Entering the city at night, Albuquerque's troops destroyed its fortifications and massacred the population. Soon the Portuguese had built a fort of their own, and asserted their control over the most vital sea-lane between Europe and Asia. Despite the opposition of Islamic sultanates in Aceh (northern Sumatra), Johor (on the southern tip of the Malay Peninsula), and western Java, the Portuguese consolidated their control of trade; their armed ships forced merchant vessels, at gunpoint, to call at Melaka as they passed through the Strait. But Melaka gradually declined under Portuguese control, for their intolerance frightened away many foreign merchants.

Portuguese power in Southeast Asia was soon challenged by the Spanish, as the fleet of Ferdinand Magellan reached the East Indies in 1523 on its way around the world. (When Magellan's fleet sailed west from Lisbon in 1521, it included a Javanese sailor; when the fleet reached Java from the east two years later, the sailor thus became the first person in history to complete a voyage around the world.) In 1529, the Portuguese and Spanish settled their differences in the Treaty of Zaragossa, which gave Spain control of the Philippines and confirmed Portugal's monopoly in the Moluccas (also called the Spice Islands). Portugal went on to establish trade links with China (at Macau) and Japan (at Nagasaki) in the 1550's.

Portugal's domination of Europe's trade with Asia was not to last. The Spanish developed a flourishing trade network with the Philippines via Mexico that bypassed the Indian Ocean route altogether. And soon, two new rivals entered the scene. The British East India Company, chartered in 1600, and the Dutch East India Company, chartered in 1602, brought Europe's two most powerful maritime nations to chal-

The buildings of Melaka's Old Town serve as a virtual museum of early European influence in Malaya. They include a Portuguese fort and church (which once held the tomb of St. Francis Xavier), this Dutch-period church and other public buildings, an English fort, and a foreign cemetery.

lenge Portuguese power in the Indies. (See *The Land and People of the Netherlands.*)

In the early decades of the seventeenth century, England concentrated on India, while the Dutch established themselves as the dominant power in Java, developing trade routes and fortified trading stations throughout the Indies and as far afield as Taiwan. A British trading station was briefly established in Ambon, in the Spice Islands, but British ambitions in the Spice Islands soon ended when Ambon was sacked by the Dutch in 1623 and all its English merchants were slaughtered. In 1641 the Dutch drove the Portuguese from Melaka, and established their own rule there for the next 150 years.

The Royal Court of Brunei

Ferdinand Magellan (1480–1521), a Portuguese navigator who served under Admiral Albuquerque in India, was given a commission in 1518 by King Charles V of Spain to make the first voyage in history around the world. Sailing westward from Spain in 1519 with five ships, Magellan reached the Philippines two years later. He was killed there in a battle with the forces of a local ruler, but the other members of the expedition continued on in one of the two ships that still remained seaworthy at that time; the other was wrecked trying to return to South America. Aboard the final ship was a young officer named Antonio Pigafetta, who later compiled a chronicle of the voyage. Here, Pigafetta describes the reception he and his shipmates received in Brunei in July 1521:

When we arrived at the city [Brunei], we remained about two hours in the ship until two elephants covered with silk came, and twelve men, each with a porcelain jar covered with silk, to carry our gifts. Then we mounted the elephants, and the twelve men marched ahead with the jars and gifts. And so we went to the governor's house, where we were given a supper of divers viands, and at night we slept on cotton mattresses. Next day we remained in the house until noon. Then we went to the king's palace on said elephants, with the gifts ahead, as on the previous day. Between the house and the king's palace all the streets were full of people with swords, spears and targets, for the king had willed it thus. Then we mounted the steps, accompanied by the governor and other notables. And we entered a large hall full of barons and lords, where we were seated on a carpet with the gifts and vessels with us.

At the head end of this hall was another one, higher but not so large, and all hung with silk drapery, and from it two windows with crimson curtains opened, by which light entered the hall. Three hundred naked men were standing there with swords and sharp stakes posed at their thigh to guard the king. And at the end of this hall was a window, and when a crimson curtain was drawn, we perceived within the king seated at a table, with one of his little sons, and they were chewing betel. Behind him were only many ladies. Then one of the chief men told us that we could not speak to the king, but that if we desired anything we should tell him, and he would tell a more notable man, who would communicate it to one of the governor's brothers, who was in the smaller hall, and he would speak through a speaking tube by a hole in the wall to the one who was inside with the king. And he instructed us that we were to make three obeisances to the king with hands clasped above our head, raising our feet one after the other since we had to kiss them.

All this was done, after the manner of their royal obeisance. And we told him that we were servants of the King of Spain, who desired peace with him and required no more than to do trade. The king caused us to be told that since the King of Spain was his friend, he was very willing to be his, and he ordered that we should be allowed to take water and wood and merchandise at our will. . . .

That city is all built in salt water, except the king's house, and the houses of certain chief men. And it has twenty or twenty-five thousand hearths. All their houses are of wood, and built on great beams raised from the ground. And when the tide is high, the women go ashore in boats to sell and buy the things necessary for their food. In front of the king's house is a thick wall of brick, with towers in the manner of a fortress, and in it were fifty-six large brass cannon. . . .

From Antonio Pigafetta, *Magellan's Voyage*, transl. and ed. by R. A. Skelton. New Haven: Yale University Press, 1969, pp. 100-101.

Although long-distance trade through the Strait of Malacca was almost wholly in the hands of European powers after 1511, European civilization had surprisingly little impact on Malaya itself over the next three hundred years. The Portuguese, and then the Dutch, were content to control trade through their fortified city of Melaka, trading with Malay, Chinese, and Indian merchants there, making little effort to settle, or even explore, the interior of the Peninsula. Whether in Malay or European hands, Melaka had always been a port of foreign trade, of little interest or importance to most Malays. The land itself was controlled by a number of small Islamic sultanates, some (such as Johor) powerful and wealthy, most poor and obscure. The only important long-term effect of the European occupation of Melaka was to strengthen these small kingdoms by forcing them to look more inland rather than to the seacoast. Not until the advent of the British at the beginning of the nineteenth century would Malaya feel the full weight of European colonialism.

The Colonial Era

The Dutch capture of Melaka in 1641 once more relegated the Malay Peninsula to the sidelines of political and economic history in the East Indies. The Dutch controlled and used the port, but they were most interested in building up their main colonial base at Batavia (now Jakarta), in Java. Consequently they diverted as much trade as possible from Melaka (and from Brunei and other small ports) to Batavia, leaving the Peninsula and northern Borneo to lapse into a period of sleepy insignificance.

This change paved the way for a further rise on a purely local scale of the sultanates of the Peninsula. The Sultan of Johor, especially, tried to build up his own realm as an independent trading center outside the sphere of European control. The other leading native kingdom at the time was Aceh, in northern Sumatra. Had Aceh and Johor united against the Dutch, they might possibly have been able to drive them from the Strait of Malacca, at least temporarily. But the two sultanates were traditional enemies, and they were never able to form an alliance against the Europeans.

The Sultan of Johor recruited Bugis mercenaries from Sulawesi in the late seventeenth century to help him maintain his independence from the Dutch and to fight the Acehnese. Rather than returning home after their services were no longer needed, the Bugis mercenaries stayed on in Johor and by 1720 had achieved effective political control over the sultanate. They also established their own independent sultanate in Selangor, waged war on the Sultan of Kedah, and formed an alliance with the sultanate of Perlis. The effect of all of this maneuvering was to force the Peninsula sultanates to defend their own territories and to pay more attention to consolidating their power.

The British

During the eighteenth century, trade between Great Britain and China grew rapidly, spurred by a growing English thirst for tea and by the rapid expansion of the British East India Company in India. By the last quarter of the century, British ships carrying opium from India to China and tea, porcelain, silk, and other goods from China to India, and thence to England, dominated sea traffic in the Strait of Malacca. (See *The Land and People of China.*) Under those circumstances, the British East India Company felt an urgent need to acquire its own base near the Strait, and ideally to oust the Dutch from Melaka.

During the seventeenth century the British had maintained a trading station at Bantam (now Benten), on the northwestern tip of Java, but they were driven out by the Dutch in 1682. They also controlled the small port of Bencoolen (now Bengkulu), on the southwestern coast of

Time Line: Malaya and Northern Borneo, 1819–1909

1819   Singapore founded; ceded to British by Sultan of Johor, 1824

1824   Anglo-Dutch treaty gives Indonesia to Dutch, Malaya to British

1841   Sarawak rebellion; James Brooke made governor of Sarawak by Sultan of Brunei

1846   Brooke proclaims himself Rajah of Sarawak

1857   First tin mines at Kuala Lumpur

1865   Brunei leases Sabah to American company

1867   Straits Settlements placed under authority of British Colonial Office

1874   Beginning of Resident system in Malay sultanates

1875   Perak War

1877   Treaties with sultans of Brunei and Sulu give outright control of Sabah to Dent Brothers

1881   British North Borneo Company founded

1888   Sarawak, Brunei, and North Borneo become British Protectorates

1896   Federated Malay States formed

LATE 19TH CENT.   Rubber plantations established in Malaya

1909   Control of Unfederated Malay States transferred from Siam to Great Britain

Sumatra, but that was on the opposite side of Sumatra from the Strait of Malacca. Ships calling at Bencoolen had to use the Sunda Strait instead to pass back and forth to the South China Sea, obliging them to sail virtually in front of the guns of the Dutch fort at Batavia.

In 1786, Sir Francis Light concluded a treaty with the Sultan of Kedah that gave the East India Company control of the island of Penang in return for supporting the Sultan against the Thai kingdom of Ayuthaya to the north. In 1798 the British also took control of the territory that they named Province Wellesley, on the coast of the Peninsula opposite Penang. The British rapidly developed Penang, encouraging Chinese immigrants to come to the nearly unpopulated island to serve as dock workers and laborers, and Chinese merchants soon followed. George Town, the island's main settlement, soon became essentially a Chinese town with British administrators. Yet Penang was not entirely satisfactory as a British base. Its harbor is neither large nor sheltered from bad weather, and the timber on the island proved unsuitable for repairing ships. Most importantly, it was too far from the narrowest stretch of the Strait of Malacca, which was still controlled by the Dutch.

The strengthening of the British position in and near Malaya came as an indirect result of events in Europe. The Netherlands were conquered by France in 1794–1795. Napoleon Bonaparte's brother Louis was crowned King of Holland in 1806. The British therefore considered the Netherlands and all of its colonies as enemies, part of the Napoleonic Empire with which it was at war. The British East India Company decided to do its part for the British war effort by attacking Dutch possessions in the East Indies.

The British briefly took possession of the Dutch East Indies, from 1811 to 1815. In 1819, over Dutch protests, Sir Thomas Stamford Raffles, who had been the British governor of Java during those years, founded a British trading settlement at Singapore, rented from the

Sultan of Johor. In 1824, the Sultan granted the island of Singapore to the East India Company as an outright possession. In that same year, the British and Dutch concluded the Treaty of London, settling their differences in the East Indies. The British gave up their trading post at Bencoolen and recognized Dutch control of the islands that now make up Indonesia, while the Dutch turned Melaka over to the British and dropped their protests about the establishment of the British settlement at Singapore.

Singapore was an immediate success. Chinese contract laborers were imported to serve as construction workers, dockhands, and porters; Chinese merchants soon followed. From a few hundred fishing families in 1819, the population of Singapore grew to 5,000 in 1820 and exceeded 80,000 by 1860. Singapore was run as a free port, meaning that ships of any nationality were able to trade there free of tariffs or other trade barriers. This made it a favorite stopping place for ships engaged in trade from Europe or India to China, and contributed to its rapid growth. Singapore soon replaced Penang as the most important British outpost east of India. In 1824 Penang, Province Wellesley, Melaka, and Singapore were joined administratively as the Straits Settlements; Dindings, another settlement south of Province Wellesley, was added in 1874. Their governor reported to the East India Company's office in Calcutta, which ruled India on behalf of the British government.

The White Rajahs of Sarawak

The British East India Company lost its legal monopoly of British trade to China in 1833. After that, the East India Company government in India paid little attention to the Straits Settlements, which were allowed to grow at their own pace through the efforts of private British and

Sir Thomas Stamford Raffles

Raffles was born in Jamaica in 1781, on board the ship of which his father was captain. In 1795, at the age of fourteen, he went to work as a junior clerk at India House, the headquarters of the East India Company in London. In 1805 he was sent to Penang as an assistant secretary in the company's offices there. He soon became fluent in Malay and played an important role in the military planning that led to the East India Company's successful attack on Batavia in 1811. Raffles was rewarded with the governorship of Java and spent the next four years planning and instituting reforms in the colonial administration there. A self-taught man of wide-ranging interests, he spent his spare time investigating the history, archaeology, and ecology of Java.

In the peace settlement that ended the Napoleonic Wars in 1815, the British agreed to return the East Indies to the Netherlands. Raffles was recalled to England just before Batavia was turned over to the Dutch once again. (Unfortunately for the Javanese, the Dutch immediately revoked Raffles's enlightened administrative reforms.) In England Raffles wrote a history of Java and was instrumental in founding the Royal Zoological Society.

In 1818, Raffles returned to the Indies as governor of Bencoolen.

Chinese merchants. The reluctance of both the Company and the British government to become involved in any more adventures in the East Indies paved the way for the rise of one of the nineteenth century's most colorful individuals, Sir James Brooke.

By the early nineteenth century, the consolidation of Dutch power at

In 1819, he persuaded the Sultan of Johor to give the East India Company a lease on a deserted island at the southern tip of the Malay Peninsula. Raffles revived the name of Singapore for the island, but the old Ayuthaya Empire settlement that once had existed there was long gone. Raffles saw, however, that the island's excellent harbor held great promise for the development of a trading base, and he moved rapidly to build a settlement there. He wrote,

Our object is not territory but trade; a great commercial emporium and a fulcrum whence we may extend our influence politically as circumstances may hereafter require. . . . One free port in these seas must eventually destroy the spell of Dutch monopoly: and what Malta is in the West, that may Singapore be in the East.

Raffles was not always popular with his superiors in India and London. He often exceeded his orders and acted on his own authority. When the Dutch protested in 1819 that the British settlement at Singapore was illegal, the British Prime Minister complained that Raffles had risked getting England involved in another war with the Netherlands. Raffles was recalled to England in 1823 and died there in 1826, disappointed that the British government had not supported his efforts to make Great Britain the supreme power in the Indies. He is remembered now as an ambitious but farsighted and capable man, the founder of Singapore.

Batavia had thoroughly undermined the sultanate of Brunei. The town of Brunei had become a sleepy backwater, and its sultan was unable to maintain control even over his own provincial governors elsewhere in northern Borneo. One of them, the governor of Sarawak, rebelled against the sultan in 1841. A British adventurer, James Brooke, who happened to be in the area, offered his services to the sultan in organizing the fight against the rebel governor. Brooke had been born in India and served in the East India Company army in Burma; he had done well enough to buy a yacht and sail to Borneo looking for ways to improve his fortune. Brooke's forces won, and in return he was given a grant of land in Sarawak, and the title of governor. Over the next few years he persuaded the sultan to grant him additional territory, including a sliver of land that gave Sarawak access to Brunei Bay at the town of Limbang, thereby splitting the Sultanate of Brunei into two parts.

In 1846, Brooke proclaimed himself Rajah of Sarawak, and announced that his kingdom would thereafter be independent of Brunei and subject to the authority of no other country. This rather astonishing act, whereby a private individual created a new, independent country with himself as its monarch, was not challenged by the British government, which had no intention of getting involved in Borneo and risking new conflict with the Dutch. Yet Brooke was crafty enough to realize that as an Englishman, he would almost certainly be defended by the British anyway if the Dutch tried to attack him. The Dutch realized that too, and refrained from interfering. The independent state of Sarawak was born.

Brooke built a fort and a small *astana* (palace) at Kuching, and invited a group of Scottish businessmen to set up the Borneo Company, Ltd., to which he gave a royal charter to conduct business. The company soon established coal mines near Kuching, to supply the steamships that were beginning to replace sailing ships in international trade, and also dealt in wood, pepper, and other traditional products of Sarawak. As a major shareholder in the Borneo Company, Brooke shared some of its profits, while his government collected taxes on the company's holdings. Sarawak soon became a prosperous undertaking.

Brooke maintained good relations with the British government,

James Brooke, the first "White Rajah" of Sarawak. He and his descendants ruled Sarawak from 1841 to 1946.

The Ranee of Sarawak

In her memoirs, the Ranee of Sarawak (the wife of Sir Charles Brooke, the second Rajah) wrote with genuine affection of the country and its people, and with open admiration for what she regarded as her husband's enlightened rule there. In retrospect her views seem extremely paternalistic and condescending, but in her own time they would have been regarded as open-minded and generous.

Some months had gone by since the day of my first arrival in Kuching and, odd as it may seem, Europe and all its ways were relegated as it were to an almost imperceptible background in my memory. The charm of the people, the wonderful beauty of the country, the spaciousness, and the absence of anything like conventionality, all enchanted me. Moreover, the people were my own, and every day that passed . . . little by little I lost some of my European ideas, and became more of a mixture between a Dyak and a Malay. The extraordinary idea which English people entertain as to an insuperable bar existing between the white and coloured races, even in those days of my youth, appeared to me to be absurd and nonsensical. Here were these people, with hardly any ideas of the ways of Europeans, who came to me as though they were my own brothers and sisters. They must have thought some of my ways curious and strange, but instead of finding fault with them, they gave way to me in everything. I suppose they saw how ready I was to care for them and consider them as members of my family, and as the country became more familiar to me, little by little, much as when one develops photographic plates, some hitherto unperceived trait in their character came out and charmed me.

From *My Life in Sarawak*, by the Ranee of Sarawak (1913). By permission of Methuen & Co., publishers.

The Fort at Kuching, Sarawak. Colonial administrative towns in Asia consisted of a "European settlement," with comfortable Western-style buildings for the rulers, and a "Native town" for the local inhabitants.

which granted him a knighthood and in 1857 made him governor of Labuan, an island off the Borneo coast northeast of Brunei, which fell under the jurisdiction of the Straits Settlements. Although Brooke established his control over Sarawak with relative ease, his rule was not unchallenged. There were occasional Iban and Kenyah uprisings over, for example, Brooke's efforts to wipe out head-hunting, and there were also violent clashes between the Iban and the Chinese workers at Brooke's coal mines. Kuching was destroyed in a Chinese rebellion in 1857, but Rajah Brooke defeated the rebels and rebuilt his palace before dying in 1868. He was succeeded by his nephew, Sir Charles Johnson Brooke, under whose rule Sarawak flourished still more.

The Tin Rush

For fifty years after the formation of the Straits Settlements, the East India Company government of India contented itself with the encour-

Head-Hunting

Head-hunting was a form of ritualized warfare widely practiced by tribal societies in Borneo, the Moluccas, and New Guinea until as recently as two or three generations ago. The colorful and somewhat shocking term applied to the practice by Europeans reflected their horror at what they regarded as a system of organized murder, but to the tribes themselves it was a normal part of life.

Specific rituals and customs associated with head-hunting varied widely from tribe to tribe, but the basic pattern was the same everywhere. Reflecting the simple political organization of tribal society, neighboring villages or longhouses would form loose alliances and sometimes conduct raids against more distant groups of people. Those raids had, in part, the objective of taking booty or winning control over land and resources, but they also involved the specific aim of killing enemies and cutting off their heads. The heads were brought back home, where they were smoked and dried, placed in ceramic jars, or otherwise treated with ceremonial dignity, and then hung up in the rafters of the longhouse for display. It was believed that the spirit of the slain enemy would then be at the service of the person who killed him, increasing that person's own power. In many tribal societies, a boy could not be considered a man until he had killed at least one enemy and brought home his head.

Because each killing created a social desire for revenge, a cycle of raids and counterraids continued indefinitely. Feuds might go on for generations. Some anthropologists have speculated that head-hunting may have served a useful purpose by limiting population growth in areas where resources were scarce. Others point out that stylized combat between adult males is widespread in mammals, from seals to deer; it is beneficial in evolutionary terms by ensuring that strong, intelligent males survive to breed, while weaker ones produce few or no offspring. Another theory about head-hunting holds that it served to reinforce social organization by channeling aggression in well-defined, socially acceptable ways, and by reinforcing the authority of men who showed leadership ability in battle. Perhaps the correct view is that head-hunting served all those purposes, and also demonstrates the nearly endless variety of social beliefs and practices of which people are capable.

When tribal areas in Borneo came under British colonial rule, the new rulers were outraged by head-hunting and made vigorous efforts to stop it. They attempted whenever possible to arrest and punish people involved in head-hunting; the tribes, in turn outraged by what they regarded as gross interference in their own traditional affairs, sometimes reacted by rebelling against and massacring the foreign rulers. Gradually the superior weaponry and organizational skills of the colonial authorities prevailed; head-hunting became more and more a rare and secret practice, and finally died out altogether.

In some longhouses in Sarawak today, ancient skulls still dangle in baskets from the rafters overhead. Embarrassed at possibly being thought "uncivilized" but also proud of the bravery and fighting skill of their ancestors, longhouse people will sometimes point out to visitors these relics of a bygone age.

agement of British trade in the Strait of Malacca and made no effort to become involved with the native rulers of Malaya. British businessmen in the Straits Settlements made some private investments in the interior of Malaya, concluding agreements with the various sultans; they often petitioned Calcutta and London to take a more active role in protecting their interests, but to no avail. Meanwhile the Chinese population of Penang, Melaka, and Singapore continued to increase, and some Chinese businessmen also moved to the Malay states in search of new opportunities. Many of them engaged in small-scale tin mining and got rich when the world market for tin suddenly expanded in the 1860's.

A practical method for preserving food in tin-plated steel cans had been perfected in the mid-nineteenth century. The American Civil War suddenly created a huge demand for tin cans, which allowed soldiers in the field to eat decent rations for perhaps the first time in history. Tin, which formerly had been used mainly for pewter and bronze, suddenly became a basic industrial commodity, and the race to develop the tin mines of Malaya began.

Even before the "tin rush" of the 1860's, tin mining in Malaya was dominated by the Chinese, who had the capital, the technical skill, and the business networks to succeed at prospecting and mining. Malaya, and especially the sultanates of Selangor and Perak, where the richest tin deposits were found, was suddenly overrun with miners staking claims and opening mines. The sultans tried to maintain some degree of control, but their underfunded and underpoliced governments were no match for the miners. In the absence of any other real control in the mining regions, power soon passed to Chinese secret societies, who set up what amounted to private governments within the sultans' own territories.

These secret societies combined some features of religious and fraternal orders, welfare organizations, and organized crime syndicates; they were somewhat like the traditional Mafia of Sicily. Members paid dues

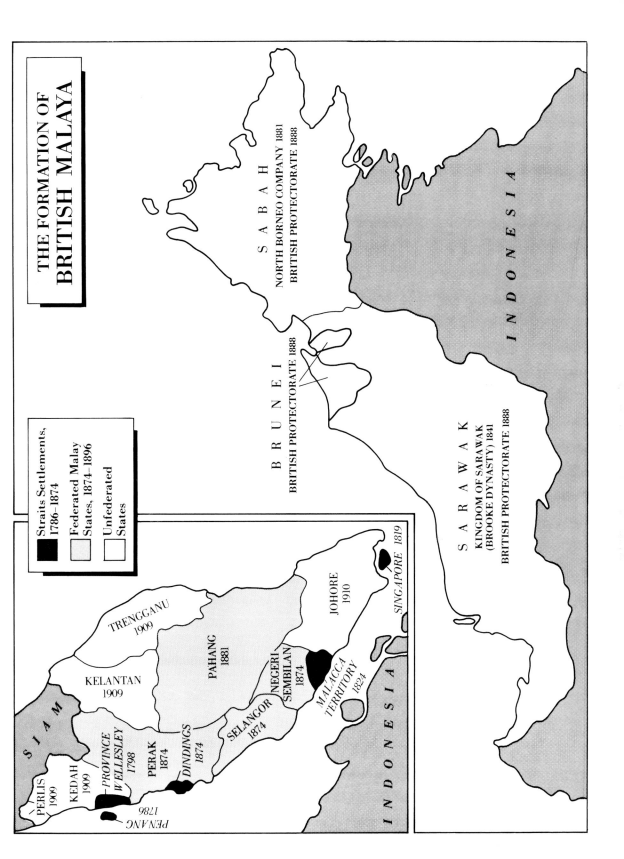

THE FORMATION OF BRITISH MALAYA

Straits Settlements, 1786–1874

Federated Malay States, 1874–1896

Unfederated States

SABAH

NORTH BORNEO COMPANY 1881
BRITISH PROTECTORATE 1888

BRUNEI

BRITISH PROTECTORATE 1888

SARAWAK

KINGDOM OF SARAWAK
(BROOKE DYNASTY) 1841
BRITISH PROTECTORATE 1888

INDONESIA

SIAM

PERLIS 1909

KEDAH 1909

PROVINCE WELLESLEY 1798

PENANG 1786

PERAK 1874

DINDINGS 1874

KELANTAN 1909

TRENGGANU 1909

PAHANG 1881

SELANGOR 1874

NEGERI SEMBILAN 1874

MALACCA TERRITORY 1824

JOHORE 1910

SINGAPORE 1819

INDONESIA

to the societies, which in turn defended their members' mining claims and other interests against outsiders. Secret societies crushed demonstrations by mine workers against mine owners who were society members, and also supported mine workers who were members in pressing for better working wages and working conditions from nonmember owners. Rival secret societies sometimes fought wars with each other. Secret societies even began to intervene in the politics of the sultanates, seeking supporters among members of the Malay aristocracy. The situation in the mining areas was out of the control of both the Malay sultans and the British authorities—one English observer described it as "bloody chaos"—and trade between the Malay states and the Straits Settlements was seriously disrupted. British businessmen, some of whom also owned tin-mining claims (usually with Chinese managers and workers), looked on with alarm, and again petitioned their government to protect their interests.

The Malay Sultanates and the Federated Malay States

By the late 1860's, the British government in any case was beginning to pay more attention to Malaya. The rapid growth of British industry during the nineteenth century had created new interest in the colonies of the British Empire, both as sources of industrial raw materials and as markets for manufactured goods. The opening of the Suez Canal in 1869 shortened the voyage between Europe and Asia and led to an increase in trade. A proposal to lay a telegraph line from India to Australia via Burma and the Malay Peninsula required stable conditions there. In 1867 the government transferred authority for the Straits Settlements from the East India Company in Calcutta to the Colonial Office in London, as a prelude to asserting greater authority in Malaya.

An energetic new governor, Sir Andrew Clarke, arrived in the Straits

Settlements in 1873. He was immediately faced with a difficult situation in Perak, where the sultan had died two years before; rival claimants to the throne, some with Chinese secret society backing, were engaged in virtual civil war. Early in 1874 some prominent Straits businessmen persuaded several Malay sultans to sign a letter asking Clarke to intervene in the situation. Clarke supported the claim of one of the rivals,

British troops attack a Malay village during the Perak War of 1875. The symbolism in this contemporary British engraving reveals the colonial attitudes of the time: The British soldiers loom large in the foreground; they are fully clothed, armed with modern weapons, and stand their ground bravely. The Malays are depicted as being half naked and armed with spears; they rush out from the village and seem to writhe in fear and anguish. Clearly, in this view, the "natives" are no match for the forces of "civilization."

Raja Abdulla, who agreed in turn to accept a British advisor, or "Resident," and to act upon his advice in all matters except those relating to Islam and Malay *adat* (customary law). J.W.W. Birch was appointed Resident of Perak, and soon gave more advice than the new sultan had bargained for, and also detached Dindings from the Territory of Perak and added it to the Straits Settlements. Birch was assassinated in 1875, clearly on the sultan's wishes; in response, the British sent troops from India and Hong Kong. In the so-called Perak War of 1875, they seized control of the state, arrested the sultan and his coconspirators, and placed a friendly new sultan on the throne.

Under Clarke's governorship, the sultans of Selangor, Pahang, and the nine small states collectively known as Negri Sembilan also accepted British Residents. They did not always do so willingly and cheerfully, but by bribing key members of the sultans' courts and by threatening the use of military force, the British got their way. Johor did not have a Resident as such, but its sultan was advised by the governor of Singapore. The Residents brought some benefits to the sultanates; for example, British-style administration was more efficient, which improved tax revenues and control over the tin industry. In addition, problems of succession to the throne (which often arose, because the sultans had many wives and many sons) could be handled more smoothly with the Resident's intervention and arbitration. The British, in turn, gained the significant advantage of being able to work through docile and cooperative native rulers. Thus they controlled much of the country with only a small investment of manpower, money, and risk.

In 1896, Perak, Pahang, Selangor, and Negri Sembilan were organized into the Federated Malay States. Their sultans transferred much of their power to a British government, headed by a Resident-General, based in the tin-mining capital of Kuala Lumpur. In return for giving up what control they still had over their own administrations and purse

The Maharaja of Johor on a visit to England in the 1870's, a representative of the semi-Westernized Malay rulers who promoted the interests of British colonialism. He wears a turban and a jacket cut in Western style but decorated with Malay-Islamic embroidery. He holds a kris, *poorly drawn by the English artist who produced this engraving.*

strings, the sultans were permitted to rule with considerable pomp, and deal with all matters of religious or purely local interest. They became, as a result, loyal supporters of the British throne and increasingly anglicized in education, tastes, and values.

The four northernmost Malay states, Perlis, Kedah, Kelantan, and Terengganu, resisted the wave of British control in the 1870's and remained loyal instead to their powerful northern neighbor, the Thai kingdom of Siam (the successor to Ayuthaya). But in 1909 Siam signed a treaty transferring control of the four states to Great Britain. The sultans themselves were not consulted; the Sultan of Kedah complained that his country had been "bought and sold like a buffalo." Perlis, Kedah, Kelantan, and Terengganu, along with Johor a year later, were made British Protectorates—that is, they were nominally independent states with British advisors, and with military affairs and foreign policy under British control. These five protectorates collectively became known as the Unfederated Malay States.

By 1909, Great Britain controlled all of Malaya, but under three separate administrative structures—the Straits Settlements, the Federated Malay States, and the Unfederated States. In the 1920's and 1930's the British government tried several times to create a single structure of colonial rule to replace the three separate systems. Such attempts were resisted both by the British/Chinese Straits Settlements, which did not want to become part of a Malay-majority federation, and by the Unfederated States, which did not want to give up any more of their freedom; the plans therefore came to nothing.

North Borneo

In 1865, an American speculator persuaded the Sultan of Brunei to grant him a lease on the northeastern tip of Borneo, the state now known as Sabah. His plans to develop the territory failed, and he soon sold his lease to a British company called Dent Brothers. In 1877, Dent Brothers negotiated a new agreement with the Sultan of Brunei giving them outright control of the territory; just to be on the safe side, they concluded an identical agreement with the Sultan of Sulu, in the Philippines, who also claimed Sabah. In 1881, Dent Brothers formed a new company, the British North Borneo Chartered Company, and obtained a royal charter from the British government to administer the territory. The company ran British North Borneo, as Sabah was then called, as a kind of private colony until 1946. As such, North Borneo was run for profit, and the North Borneo Company's harsh policies were strongly resented by the people under its rule. Mat Salleh, Sabah's national hero, was a Bajau prince who led a fierce rebellion against the North Borneo Company in 1895. He was killed by the North Borneo police in 1900, but the rebellion continued for another five years after his death.

In 1888, Sarawak, British North Borneo, and Brunei were all made British Protectorates, the same arrangement that was later to govern the Unfederated Malay States. By intervening in that way, the British government was able to insist on the peaceful settlement of competing territorial claims that had developed between Sarawak and North Borneo, and also to prevent Brunei from being swallowed up altogether by its two larger neighbors. As British Protectorates, Sarawak continued to be an independent kingdom and North Borneo a company colony, while Brunei was left as an impoverished and isolated sultanate. Ironically, when oil was discovered on the northern coast of Borneo in 1929, it was on the tiny bit of land that Brunei had been left with; the Sultan of Brunei soon became one of the richest men in Asia.

British Colonial Rule

The international rubber boom that came with the opening of the Automobile Age soon made Malaya one of Great Britain's most prosperous colonial possessions. The development of a plantation economy was part of a larger British design for running Malaya in a way that was orderly and peaceful as well as profitable. But British colonial rule also proved to have some long-term negative social and economic effects.

The British (and a few other Europeans) in Malaya lived in cities as administrators, in the Straits Settlements towns of Penang, Melaka, and Singapore as international businessmen, or in houses on their rubber estates. They developed a comfortable, secure, and rather smug colonial life, complete with houses full of servants, grand public buildings, and private "whites-only" clubs. They congratulated themselves that Malaya was known as the "pearl" of the British Empire; they complained about what crafty businessmen the Chinese were, and talked condescendingly about the charming customs of the Malay natives. The Indians they ignored altogether.

Divide and Rule

By 1909, when the British colonial administration in Malaya was completely in place, Malaya was already a multiracial society. During the first thirty years of the twentieth century, a sharp increase in the number of Chinese and Indian immigrant workers exaggerated the country's ethnic pluralism still further; thousands of Malay-speaking immigrants also arrived from the East Indies at the same time and were absorbed into the local Malay population. The British used this situation to employ a "divide and rule" policy in their dealings with the Malays, the Chinese, and the Indians. They were careful to run the country in

Indian workers tapping rubber trees on a plantation in Malaya during the 1920's. Their descendants are very likely doing the same work today. From Frank G. Carpenter, *Java and the East Indies,* Garden City, NY: Doubleday & Company, Inc., 1926, facing p. 242, courtesy of Mrs. Edith H. Williams and Mrs. Joanna H. Noel.

Somerset Maugham

The British writer Somerset Maugham (1874–1965) first visited Malaya as an intelligence agent during the First World War, and he returned several times in the 1920's. Many of his novels and short stories are set in Malaya, and he became famous as a keen observer of the customs—and scandals—of the British colonial population there. He portrayed their lives as being wealthy and privileged, but also narrow and unsatisfying, hemmed in by racial prejudice, class barriers, and a sense of alienation from their adopted country.

Maugham's description of the Malacca Club, during colonial times a for-whites-only establishment, captures perfectly the flavor of colonial life. The following quotation, framed, still hangs on the wall of the now-integrated clubhouse:

The club faces the sea; it is a spacious but shabby building; it has an air of neglect and when you enter you feel that you intrude. It gives you the impression that it is closed really, for alterations and repairs, and that you have taken indiscreet advantage of an open door to go where you are not wanted. In the morning you may find there a couple of planters who have come in from their estates on business and are drinking a gin-sling before starting back again; and latish in the afternoon a lady or two may perhaps be seen looking with a furtive air through old numbers of the "Illustrated London News." At nightfall a few men saunter in and sit about the billiard-room watching the play and drinking sukus. But on Wednesdays there is a little more animation. On that day the gramophone is set going in the large room upstairs and people come in from the surrounding country to dance. There are sometimes no less than a dozen couples and it is even possible to make up two tables of bridge.

From "Footsteps in the Jungle," in *Ah King* (1933), pp.6–7. By permission of A.P. Watt Ltd., on behalf of The Royal Literary Fund.

a way calculated to prevent the rise of a united anti-British and anticolonial nationalism, on the one hand, and to prevent racial discord on the other.

By law, agricultural land could not be sold to non-Malays. Malays therefore became a people of courts and *kampungs*; the elite ran the governments of the sultanates under British protection (and were often corrupted and exploited by their British advisors), while commoners remained farmers, fisherfolk, and laborers.

The Chinese controlled tin mining and most local commerce; some became farmers or rubber planters, but most lived in cities and towns and were businessmen, ranging from shopkeepers to wealthy company owners.

The British could not own agricultural land, but they could obtain timber concessions from state governments and cut down forests; when the forests were logged over, the land could then be planted with rubber trees. Most rubber plantations were developed by British businessmen in that way; half of the land devoted to rubber plantations was owned by just five British companies in the early twentieth century. The rubber plantations were worked by Indian laborers, who were brought from Tamil Nadu under work contracts that made them little more than hired slaves.

One effect of these racially based policies was to harden the lines that divided Malays, Chinese, and Indians. The Straits Chinese and the Melaka Portuguese had shown in an earlier period that racial amity and cultural exchange was possible in Malaya; under British rule, however, ethnic separateness was encouraged. For example, Kuala Lumpur was officially divided into racially defined neighborhoods. Intermarriage between members of different groups was discouraged and made difficult by official regulations. The British authorities preferred to rule as much as possible through native leaders, and these too were chosen from within separate ethnic groups: Malay sultans, Chinese trade-

association leaders and labor bosses, Indian rubber-estate foremen.

Education provides one of the clearest examples of how the British authorities promoted ethnic pluralism. Rather than devising a unified educational system for Malaya, they encouraged different groups to establish their own schools. Thus there were Malay schools, often sponsored by Islamic religious organizations; Chinese schools in which the language of instruction was usually Mandarin;* and Indian schools, taught in Tamil, Gujarati, and other Indian languages. The effect of this was to encourage all Malay speakers (Peninsular Malays, Minangkabaus, Bugis, Javanese immigrants) to think of themselves as "Malays," all Chinese speakers (Straits Chinese, Cantonese, Hokkiens, and others) to think of themselves as "Chinese"—in other words, a previously fluid and diverse ethnic situation became more sharply polarized. Moreover, children of elite members of all three groups frequently attended missionary schools taught in English, or even went to England for a private education, creating an anglicized upper class sympathetic to the culture and outlook of the British colonial rulers. A similar system of ethnically based private schools continues to operate alongside the public schools (taught in Malay) in Malaysia today, with the same effect of reinforcing the ethnic divisions within Malaysian society.

---

*Mandarin, spoken widely throughout northern China, has come to be accepted as China's standard national spoken language. Most Chinese in Malaya spoke one or another southern dialect, such as Cantonese, Hakka, or Hokkien. Written Chinese does not vary regardless of spoken dialect.

A tin mine in Malaya in the 1920's. Gravel washed from the soil by water under high pressure (note the long pipe) flows through a channel where particles of tin settle out. The tin is then processed by the plant in the background. Most of the workers are Chinese, identified by their conical hats and shoulder carrying poles. Note the damage done to the landscape by this type of mining. From Frank G. Carpenter, *Java and the East Indies*, facing p. 247, courtesy of Mrs. Edith H. Williams and Mrs. Joanna H. Noel.

Baba-Nyonya Culture

The "Straits Chinese" of Melaka and other towns on the Strait of Malacca along the west coast of the Malay Peninsula form an old and tightly knit community with a unique culture of its own. Descended, in many cases, from ancestors who arrived several centuries ago, before the beginning of the British colonial era, they dominated the commercial life of the region. Known as "Baba-Nyonya" (literally, "master-mistress," as they were called by their Malay servants) culture, their way of life was a blend formed over many generations of Chinese and Malay elements. The Straits Chinese became fully bilingual, using Chinese as a written, commercial, and formal language but speaking Malay in everyday life. Similarly, their clothing, furniture, music, and entertainments combined Chinese and Malay styles. And by using Malay ingredients and Chinese cooking techniques, they created what remains today Malaysia's finest cuisine.

Many members of the present generation of Straits Chinese consider Baba-Nyonya culture to be old-fashioned and irrelevant to modern life; the traditional ways are vanishing rapidly. But the old downtown section of Melaka still has dozens of handsome old Baba-Nyonya houses that stand as a reminder of the old customs.

The Colonial Economy

Malaya's rubber boom transformed the country's rural economy from one of small, village-based farmers who were self-sufficient at a subsistence level to one of large plantation owners employing hundreds of wage

These houses, solidly built and decorated with architectural ornaments that proclaimed the wealth and good taste of the owners, follow an invariable pattern. The front of the ground floor is a shop or office, opening onto the street. Behind that is a central courtyard or atrium, adjacent to which is the kitchen and servants' quarters. Upstairs are the family rooms, with high ceilings and wide doorways to catch any breezes that might relieve the constant heat. And in the back of the house are workshops, warehouses, and loading docks fronting onto the river or one of its branch canals (many of which have now been filled in and paved over as streets).

Standing side by side for many blocks in the old town, these houses, once elegant but now mostly rather shabby, are a reminder of the wealth of Malaya's traditional economy, based on exports of raw materials and imports of finished goods from all over the world. The Baba-Nyonya culture that created the houses is a reminder, too, that Chinese and Malay culture once could, under some circumstances and to a certain extent, blend to form a new and unique mix. That possibility seems to elude Malaysia today, as the nation finds itself struggling to create a sense of national identity that might transcend the mutual suspicions and isolation of its various ethnic groups.

laborers, and of plantation smallholders with limited resources. Malaya's rural population as a whole became more dependent on imported food and consumer goods, as land was shifted from food production to rubber (and later palm oil) production, and it also became highly vulnerable to international fluctuations in the prices of plantation products.

The river port of Kuching, Sarawak, in a photograph from the late nineteenth century—
about the time when Joseph Conrad was writing his novels set in the East Indies. From
My Life in Sarawak, by the Ranee of Sarawak, facing p. 62. By permission of Methuen & Co.,
publishers.

Many rural Malays were poorer and less well nourished during the
British colonial period than they had been earlier under their traditional
sultans. Rather than growing most of their own food, as they had done
in the past, they depended on agricultural wages or earnings from
small-scale rubber production for money to buy food. If the price of
rubber declined, their earnings, and their diet, suffered.

In addition, the colonial administration ensured that land taxes were
collected more efficiently than they had been under the precolonial
sultans, at least from small landowners; large landowners frequently
had enough political clout to get their tax assessments reduced. The

authorities also were creative in thinking up new sources of tax revenue. For example, the government collected a concession tax from merchants who were licensed to sell opium; that provided a significant amount of tax revenue for the government, but tended to impoverish further the people who turned to opium for relief from their troubles.

British colonial rule was intended above all to benefit England itself; it also served the economic interests of large plantation owners, mine owners, and merchants—of all ethnic groups—in Malaya. It was much less effective in protecting the interests of ordinary farmers, workers, and small business owners. For example, Malaya's economy was devastated when international prices for rubber and tin collapsed during the Great Depression of the 1930's; the biggest plantation and mine owners had the financial and political resources to avoid bankruptcy, but many small businesses collapsed, and tens of thousands of rubber workers and miners lost their jobs.

Still, if many people had reason to resent British colonial rule in Malaya, many others accepted it without protest. From 1909 to 1942 Malaya was on the whole stable and well run, at least by the standards of other colonies in the Third World during the Age of Empire. Life was comfortable for many of its people, though precarious for the "underclass" of Indian rubber tappers, Malay farmers, and Chinese laborers. The British in Malaya enjoyed their colonial privileges and made little impression on the rest of the world. The Malays, Chinese, and Indians seemed on the surface content under British rule, although considerable resentment of both the British and of other races percolated beneath the surface among all three groups. It seemed that things could continue to go smoothly indefinitely, until suddenly World War II changed everything.

Nationalism and Independence

December 7, 1941, is famous in America as the day Japan bombed Pearl Harbor. Few Americans remember that on the same day, the Japanese launched simultaneous attacks on Manila and Hong Kong. Singapore, the other great center of Anglo-American power in Asia, was beyond the reach of Japanese bombers, but on December 8 Japanese troops landed on the east coast of Malaya and raced south through the Peninsula. Singapore fell on February 15, 1942, and the Japanese conquest of all of Malaya was complete by the end of March. Japanese troops also landed in Sarawak, Brunei, and British North Borneo early in 1942, and those territories surrendered after offering only brief resistance. The British colonial era in Malaya had come to a sudden, though temporary end. The Japanese occupation proved to be short, but it had effects that lasted long beyond the end of the war.

Time Line: Malaysia and Brunei, 1909–1990

1909   All of Malaya under British control

1920   Malayan rubber production reaches 53% of world total

1923   Singapore–Johor causeway built

1929   Oil discovered in Brunei

1930's   Great Depression; distress in rubber and tin industries

1937   Japan invades China

DEC. 8, 1941   Japanese troops land near Kota Baru

FEB.–MAR. 1942   Singapore, Malaya, Sarawak, Brunei, and North Borneo fall to Japan

AUG.–SEPT. 1945   Japan surrenders; British reoccupy Malaya; sultans cede full powers to British crown

APRIL 1, 1946   Malayan Union formed; Singapore becomes Crown Colony

MAY 1946   UMNO founded

JULY 1946   Sarawak and North Borneo become Crown Colonies

FEB. 1948   Malayan Union dissolved; Federation of Malaya established.

1948   Communist insurgency (the Emergency) begins

1951–52   The Emergency reaches its height

1952   Dato Onn leaves UMNO, forms Malayan Independence Party; Tunku Abdul Rahman becomes president of UMNO

1952   Local elections; UMNO-MCA Alliance wins

1954   Last British high commissioner for Malaya appointed

1955   First federal elections; UMNO-MCA-MIC Alliance takes 51 of 52 seats in Legislative Council. Rahman becomes chief minister

1956   Merdeka Mission to London to negotiate independence

AUG. 31, 1957   Federation of Malaya proclaimed independent nation; Rahman becomes prime minister

JUNE 1959   Singapore granted self-rule; Lee Kwan Yew becomes chief minister

JULY 1960   Emergency ends; British counterinsurgency forces leave

AUG. 1962   Plan for Federation of Malaysia announced

JULY 1963   Brunei declines to join Malaysia

SEPT. 16, 1963   Federation of Malaysia formed

APRIL 1964   National elections; Alliance increases its legislative majority

AUG. 9, 1965   Singapore withdraws from Federation of Malaysia

1967   Association of Southeast Asian Nations (ASEAN) formed

SEPT. 1967   Malay becomes sole official language of Malaysia

MAY 1969   Ethnic riots in Kuala Lumpur; state of emergency proclaimed

1970   New Economic Policy (NEP) instituted

SEPT. 21, 1970   Rahman steps down as Prime Minister, replaced by Tun Razak

1974   Barisan Nasional formed

JAN. 1976   Tun Razak dies; Datuk Hussein Onn becomes prime minister

1980   Mahathir bin Mohamad becomes prime minister

MID-1980s   Economic slump; commercial and banking scandals

1983–84   Mahathir forces constitutional changes to restrict power of king

JAN. 1, 1984   Brunei becomes an independent nation

1987   UMNO attempts illegally to prevent seating of elected Kadazan Christian government in Sabah

1990   Sultan Azlan Muhibbuddin Shah of Perak elected Malaysia's ninth king; Manhathir and UMNO win national elections; Tunku Abdul Rahman dies

Prelude to War

World War II came to Malaya in 1941, but the war itself had started long before. In Asia it began in July 1937, when Japanese and Chinese troops clashed at the Marco Polo Bridge near Beijing. Malaya's large Chinese population had eagerly been following events in China for years. Some supported the Nationalist Party of Chiang Kai-shek, others the Communists led by Mao Zedong; all hated and feared the Japanese, who it seemed never stopped trying to take over their country. (See *The Land and People of China.*) The Malayan Chinese were keenly aware of the danger that the Japanese war would spread to other parts of Asia.

For the British, World War II began in 1939, with the Nazi invasion of Poland. Many adult British men returned home to join the armed forces, and the military garrison of Singapore was reinforced. But as long as the war stayed far away, it brought benefits to Malaya as well. War created an unprecedentedly high demand for Malayan tin and rubber, and for oil from Brunei as well. For a while, Malaya's businessmen were pleased to be able to contribute to Great Britain's war efforts and to grow rich in the process.

The Japanese Occupation

The reality of war changed everything. The Japanese invasion surprised everyone by its swiftness; the country fell before there was time to mount an effective resistance. Marching down the Peninsula, Japanese troops used bicycles to transport military supplies—a technique that later would be borrowed by the North Vietnamese along the Ho Chi Minh trail. With Malaya securely in Japanese hands, the invaders quickly set up an occupation government. The country's rich natural resources were lost to the Allies and went instead to strengthen the military might of Japan.

The Japanese occupation affected Malaya's different national groups in different ways. British nationals were rounded up and placed in prisoner-of-war camps. Members of the Malay aristocracy, pro-British by education, inclination, and self-interest, were treated strictly but not brutally, for fear of alienating the Malay masses. Many Malay intellectuals and members of the small Malay middle class believed Japanese claims that Japan had liberated Malaya from British colonialism, and had instituted a policy of "Asia for the Asians." They were ready to accept the Japanese as liberators, for nationalist opposition to the exploitiveness and arrogance of British rule had already developed within Malay commercial and intellectual circles before the war. Most rural Malays were indifferent; they didn't care whether their colonial rulers were British or Japanese.

The Indian community was divided. Some Indians remained pro-British, and were treated by the Japanese as enemies. Some joined the Indian National Army, a force organized in India by the anti-British leader Subhas Chandra Bose to fight British colonialism as an ally of Japan. The burden of the occupation fell most heavily, however, on the Chinese. Having already been bogged down in a war with China for years, the Japanese considered all Chinese in Malaya to be enemy aliens, and dealt with them brutally. Many were placed in concentration camps or forced to work in the mines and plantations as slave laborers.

Treated as enemies, many Chinese chose to fight the Japanese. The Malay People's Anti-Japanese Army, the only effective guerilla resistance group in Malaya, was almost entirely Chinese and was led by members of the (Chinese) Malayan Communist Party. It was supplied secretly by British intelligence forces, and opposed by Japanese-organized local police troops, who were almost entirely ethnic Malays.

The British Return

With the defeat of Japan in August 1945, the Japanese occupation of Malaya and North Borneo collapsed. The British moved in quickly to accept the Japanese surrender and to rebuild their colonial administration. It soon became clear, however, that it would not be possible to re-create the prewar system as if nothing had happened. Many British leaders had already realized during the war that the British Empire was nearing the end of its days. In particular, plans to grant independence to the Empire's "Crown Jewel," India and Pakistan—an event that occurred in 1947—would have an obvious impact on imperial colonies farther to the east.

Moreover, the experience of the Japanese occupation had transformed Malaya. Many Malays, while abandoning their pro-Japanese sympathies, had realized that the British Empire was not invincible; having become enthusiastic about the idea of Malay nationalism, they did not welcome the return of their British rulers. Even more strikingly, many Chinese had enjoyed their taste of military power. Having been in the forefront of anti-Japanese resistance, they saw no reason why they should return to a quiet life as merchants or miners, subservient both to Malay princes and British colonial administrators. The British tried to disarm the Malay People's Anti-Japanese Army once its mission had been fulfilled, but many Chinese guerilla fighters hid their weapons for future use.

The initial British reaction, in April 1946, was to proclaim the formation of the Malayan Union, a Crown Colony comprising Penang and Melaka, the Federated States, and the Unfederated States (Singapore, with its Chinese majority, would become a separate Crown Colony). Under this plan, the sultans were to lose their right to rule, and Malayan citizenship would be granted to all of the Crown Colony's people, regardless of ethnic identity. The Malays responded a month later by forming the United Malays National Organization (UMNO), led by members of the ruling family of Johor, to preserve the primacy of the Malays in the country's national life. Faced with strikes, boycotts, and demonstrations, the British backed down. They agreed to negotiate with UMNO—itself a victory for the Malay leaders—and to come up with a new plan for the country's future.

Meanwhile, in Borneo, the third Rajah of Sarawak, Charles Vyner Brooke, overruled the objections of his heir-apparent and in 1946 transferred sovereignty over Sarawak to the British government; Sarawak thereafter became a British Crown Colony. At the same time, the British North Borneo Company transferred its private colony to the British government, and British North Borneo became a Crown Colony as well. Brunei remained a British Protectorate.

In February 1948 the British government announced the formation of the Malayan Federation, which replaced the Malayan Union. The powers of the sultans were restored, and many special provisions were instituted to ensure that the Malays would retain their paramount position in land owning and in the government bureaucracy. This satisfied the aims of UMNO, but many members of Malaya's Chinese population were outraged. Considering that they had been allies of the British in the fight against Japan, while many Malays had been Japanese collaborators, they felt that they deserved to be rewarded for their efforts, not relegated to second-class citizenship once again. The Malayan Chinese Association (MCA) was formed in 1949 to defend Chinese interests against the claims of UMNO, which by then had assumed the leading role in Malayan political affairs. The Indians, who were mostly rural and impoverished, had little say in these matters, one way or another. Their leaders, who had formed the Malayan Indian Congress in 1946, worked to protect their interests as best they could.

The Emergency

In the winter of 1948 an international conference of Communist Youth Leagues, meeting in Calcutta, issued a call to the nations of Southeast Asia to begin "wars of national liberation" against their colonial rulers. Partly in response to this, and partly because their own grievances had reached the breaking point, the Chinese-dominated Malayan Communist Party (MCP) revived the guerilla warfare units that they had sponsored during World War II, took to the jungle, and began to try to drive out the British. At the peak of the rebellion, some 9,000 armed communists were actively fighting the Malayan police force and British counterinsurgency units. The British colonial government declared a state of emergency, which was not to be lifted until 1960. A few hundred MCP guerillas continued to conduct raids against police stations and other government facilities in the northern Malay Peninsula until very recently.

The MCP rebellion, which was waged with particular ferocity until the mid-1950's, never came close to toppling British colonial rule, but it did cause considerable chaos and destruction throughout Malaya. An estimated 11,000 people died as a direct result of the fighting; bridges, railway junctions, power plants, and other facilities were destroyed. Although the number of guerilla fighters was small in comparison to the total Chinese population of Malaya, Chinese support for them was widespread, especially among the rural poor.

In response, the government armed forces devised the "Briggs Plan" (named for the British general in charge of the counterinsurgency program). This created a system of about 600 "new villages," guarded settlements surrounded by barbed wire where tens of thousands of Chinese were forced to live. This was designed to prevent the residents of the new villages from giving support to the guerillas, and to keep the Chinese population under control. About 10,000 Chinese hard-core supporters of the rebellion were deported to China. The Briggs Plan was somewhat effective, but it had the long-term consequence of alienating a large part of the Chinese population from both the British and the Malays for many years to come.

Merdeka

Despite the emergency, the British colonial government made plans to create an elected Malayan government in the 1950's, as a prelude to

Two members of a counterinsurgency unit of the Malayan Police (one British, one Chinese) question a Chinese farmer during the Communist rebellion ("the Emergency") of the early 1950's. Courtesy of the BBC Radio Hulton Picture Library/The Bettmann Archive

independence. In preparation for the elections, UMNO President Dato Onn bin Jaafar proposed that the membership of UMNO be broadened to include all of Malaya's ethnic groups. His party council disagreed, and he resigned from the party. Onn then organized a new multiethnic party, the Independence Party of Malaya. Leadership of UMNO passed to Tunku Abdul Rahman, a nephew of the Sultan of Kedah.

In municipal and city elections in 1951–52, Rahman employed a surprising strategy; he and the veteran Chinese politician Tan Cheng Lok negotiated an electoral alliance between UMNO and the Malayan Chinese Association. The alliance made sense; UMNO needed money,

The Father of Malaysian Independence

Abdul Rahman was born on February 8, 1903. His father was the
Sultan of Kedah; his mother, a Thai, was one of the sultan's several
wives. He was not in line to inherit his father's throne, which
descended to his uncle, but he had the right to use the title *tunku*
(prince), and he received a comfortable upbringing. In his early
childhood, before the transfer of the Unfederated Malay States to
British rule, Kedah was under the control of the Kingdom of Siam;
because of that, and also through his mother's influence, his early
education was in a Thai-language school. Later he attended schools
taught in Malay and in English, giving him a multilingual and
multicultural background and outlook from an early age.

In his youth, Tunku Abdul Rahman was known as a
cosmopolitan and sophisticated man, and a bit of a playboy. He
began his career in government as an administrative officer in
Kedah in 1931, and held that post until the end of the Japanese
occupation of Malaya in 1945. To the surprise of some of his
friends, he took his political career seriously and became known as
a skillful and conscientious administrator. He also became interested
in the growing Malay nationalist movement. During the final years
of the Japanese occupation, he was involved in organizing a
nationalist group called sa-Berkas (Unity). He soon dissociated
himself from it, however, because he felt that its goal of Malayan
independence immediately after the end of the war was unrealistic
and confrontational.

After the Japanese surrender, he went to England to study law,
and was admitted to the bar in 1948. Returning to Malaya, he
became one of the founders of the United Malays National

Organization (UMNO). When Dato Onn bin Jaafar, UMNO's president, split with the organization when his plan to broaden membership to include non-Malays was rejected, Tunku Abdul Rahman became president of UMNO. In 1952 he was instrumental in creating an alliance between UMNO and the main Chinese and Indian parties that has dominated Malayan politics ever since.

After the Alliance won an overwhelming victory in Malaya's first legislative elections in 1955, Tunku Abdul Rahman became the country's chief minister, still under British rule. In 1956 he undertook his celebrated "Merdeka Mission" to London to negotiate the terms of Malayan independence. When Malaya became an independent nation on August 31, 1957, Tunku Abdul Rahman gained another title: *Bapa Merdeka*, "Father of Independence."

Tunku Abdul Rahman became Malaya's first prime minister on the day the country gained its independence, and held that office until 1970. His greatest accomplishments were the formation of the Federation of Malaysia, which united Malaya with Sarawak and Sabah (and, briefly, also Singapore), and the creation and management of a constitutional regime that protected the interests of all the country's ethnic groups. His authority was badly damaged by the ethnic riots of May 1969, however, and after a year of struggle, he stepped down as prime minister. Until his death in 1990, he lived in comfortable retirement in Penang and wrote a column for *The Star*, one of Malaysia's main newspapers. In his role as the grand old man of Malaysian independence and nationalism, he argued for reasonable and pragmatic solutions to his country's difficult problems. In the words of one biographer, he was "the best of his generation."

and the MCA needed voting support. The Independence Party of Malaya, which had been widely expected to win the elections, was soundly defeated by the UMNO-MCA alliance and soon disappeared as a political force. The electoral pattern of ethnic parties entering into strategic alliances was to become a model that would endure for decades to come, dooming any chance of the emergence of genuine multiethnic parties in the Peninsula. And Tunku Abdul Rahman emerged as the undisputed leader of the Malayan independence movement.

UMNO, the MCA, and the Malayan Indian Congress (MIC) began to work seriously over the next several years to plan for independence. In 1956 Rahman traveled to London on the "*Merdeka* (freedom) Mission," to discuss the terms under which the British would grant independence to Malaya. The British made it clear that they would not accept any plan that denied basic civil rights to the Chinese and the Indians. In response, UMNO, the MCA, and the MIC negotiated an agreement known as "the Bargain." The non-Malay leaders accepted that the Malays would permanently dominate the government of an independent Malaya, and would be granted constitutional guarantees of their special position in the civil service, the armed forces, and other national organizations. Malay was to become the sole official national language ten years after independence. In return, the Malays recognized that all people born in Malaya, regardless of ethnic group, would automatically become Malayan citizens with full constitutional rights (except that their rights were sometimes limited by the constitution).

The Malayan government was to be a parliamentary system on the British model, with a bicameral legislature consisting of a House of Representatives and a Senate. The former was to initiate laws, the latter to approve them (or return them to the House of Representatives for revision). The head of government would be a prime minister, and the head of state a king, known formally as the Yang di-Pertuan Agung, elected for a five-year term by and from among the sultans of the nine Malay states (Penang and Melaka, as ex-British colonies, had no sultans).

A constitution embodying that system was written in 1957. On August 31 of that year, the government of Prime Minister Tunku Abdul Rahman, elected by an alliance of ethnic parties, proclaimed the independence of the Federation of Malaya. Malaya automatically became a member of the British Commonwealth, and was elected to the United Nations.

The Creation of Malaysia

In the national elections of 1959, UMNO was seriously challenged by a new political contender, the Partai Islam se-Malaya (PAS). Although the UMNO-led alliance retained control of the national government, Rahman began to worry about getting into a "bidding war" with the PAS over which party most successfully represented the interests of Islam in Malaya. Partly with that in mind, he began to explore the possibility of broadening the Federation of Malaya.

In 1961, Rahman proposed the creation of a new nation, Malaysia, which would unite Malaya, Singapore, and the three British-controlled territories of Sarawak, Brunei, and North Borneo. Singapore signaled its willingness to discuss the matter; although many citizens of Chinese-dominated Singapore were wary of joining a Malay-dominated federation, Singapore's leader, Lee Kwan Yew, had his own reasons for favoring the idea. His People's Action Party (PAP) was in trouble, having just split into two factions. And he saw an opportunity to broaden his own political arena from a tiny Chinese state to a great confederation that would include both the Peninsula and northern Borneo.

The Omar Ali Saifuddin Mosque, Bandar Seri Begawan. Brunei's state mosque is a grandiose symbol of the country's wealth, and of its commitment to the primacy of Islam in national life.

The British were interested, too. Sarawak and North Borneo were both poor and underdeveloped. Their economic support and military defense were a drain on the British treasury that the government was anxious to get rid of. In addition, there were emerging nationalist movements in both territories. In North Borneo (soon to be renamed Sabah), many people recalled with pride the Mat Salleh Rebellion, which had fought the British North Borneo Company for ten years from 1895 to 1905.

Negotiations over the next two years proceeded smoothly, except in the case of Brunei. The leaders of the other territories asked the Sultan of Brunei to give up to the government of the new federation a larger share of oil revenues than he was willing to part with. In addition, the sultan demanded that he be given a title superior to that of the Malayan sultans, and also that he be eligible for election to the throne of Malaysia. The Malayan sultans rejected both of those demands. Brunei withdrew from the London conference planning the Malaysian federation in July 1963. Brunei chose to remain a British Protectorate and retained that status until it won its own independence on January 1, 1984.

Despite widespread opposition in Sarawak and Sabah (where many people hoped for full independence, not membership in Malaysia), in 1962 a United Nations Malaysia Mission declared that a majority of the people in Malaya, Singapore, Sarawak, and Sabah supported union, and gave its approval to the merger plan.

The Malayan constitution was made the basis for the new federation's government, with revisions to reflect the new circumstances. For example, the guaranteed rights of Malays were extended to the *bumiputras* of northern Borneo. Singapore was treated as a special case; its citizens remained citizens of Singapore, with equal rights under the Malaysian constitution but with no rights of residence or political participation elsewhere in the federation. The Federation of Malaysia came into being on September 16, 1963.

The new state of Malaysia was strongly opposed by Indonesia, which claimed all of Borneo as its own territory. In 1964, Indonesia's President Sukarno proclaimed a policy of *konfrontasi* (confrontation) against the Malaysians in Sarawak and Sabah. The Indonesian confrontation proved to be short-lived and not terribly serious militarily, however, and its main effect was to strengthen the UMNO-led alliance. The Malaysian government was able to use patriotism as a rallying cry, offsetting the increasing gains of the PAS. The Indonesian threat faded in 1965, when a communist coup attempt and an anticommunist countercoup toppled Sukarno from power.

Exit Singapore

Singapore never fit very comfortably into the Federation of Malaysia, and strains began to appear very quickly. Most significantly, Lee Kwan Yew immediately began to challenge the leadership of Malaysia's Chinese parties, principally the MCA, in an obvious attempt to make his own PAP the dominant Chinese party in the federation. Lee confronted Rahman on a number of political issues, and the leaders of the various Malay parties warned of serious ethnic violence if Singapore's Chinese population began to play a significant role in the politics of the federation as a whole. In 1965 Rahman issued an ultimatum to Lee Kwan Yew, and on August 9, 1965, Singapore "withdrew" or "was expelled" (depending on one's point of view) from the Federation of Malaysia.

The Crisis of 1969

The separation of Singapore from Malaysia did not, however, quiet the rising tide of ethnic politics in Malaysia itself. As 1967, the year in which Malay was to become the nation's sole official language, drew near, the Chinese community protested and demanded a revision of that part of "the Bargain." Rahman responded by granting non-Malays the right to use English in official dealings with the government, rather than Malay, but by then passions were sufficiently inflamed that the Chinese were not satisfied. Many demanded that Mandarin (the language of instruction in Chinese schools, though not the native dialect of most Malaysian Chinese) be given official status also. A new and more militant Chinese party, the Democratic Action Party (DAP), challenged the

Returning in 1956 from successful negotiations in London that would lead to Malayan independence, Tunku Abdul Rahman triumphantly brandishes an antique kris.
Courtesy of Datuk Rais Yatim and the Consulate General of Malaysia

MCA for leadership in the Chinese community, and called for a policy of "Malaysia for all Malaysians."

In elections held on the Peninsula in the spring of 1969, the UMNO-led alliance retained power, but suffered serious electoral losses to nonalliance Chinese opposition parties. On May 12 the police granted permission for two Chinese parties to have a victory celebration in Kuala Lumpur. The celebration, planned as a parade, quickly turned into an unruly demonstration. The next day the police also gave permission for a Malay counterdemonstration. Truckloads of Malays were brought into the city from the countryside by political organizers. Malay peasants, waving their long *parang*s (machetelike knives), surged through the city in a rampage of ethnic violence, arson, and destruction. Hundreds of Chinese were murdered, and many more people died as police fired into crowds.

The government immediately suspended the elections in Sarawak and Sabah (which were to have been held later), declared a state of emergency, and placed the government in the hands of a National Operations Council (NOC) under Deputy Prime Minister Tun Razak. Over the next year, the NOC worked to salvage the political life of Malaysia after the watershed events of 1969. The result was that a set of amendments to the constitution was proposed (and passed in 1971), entrenching Malay ethnic rights and ensuring permanent Malay control by making any further amendments to the constitution subject to the approval of the Council of Rulers, Malaysia's nine sultans. The government also strengthened the Sedition Act, making censorship of newspapers and other public media a permanent feature of Malaysian life and prohibiting the public discussion of "sensitive" issues.

Most significantly, the government passed the New Economic Policy (NEP), which provided greatly expanded "affirmative action" programs designed to advance the interests of ethnic Malays. The rationale behind the NEP was that the guaranteed political dominance of the Malays would never be meaningful until they had advanced far enough economically to challenge Chinese control of the national economy. Malays henceforth were to receive preferential treatment in university admissions, were eligible for special government loans and grants to help them establish businesses, and were granted special status in the administration of government-owned enterprises.

Politics under the New Economic Policy

Tunku Abdul Rahman retired from politics in 1971. He was succeeded as the leader of UMNO by Tun Razak, who in 1974 announced the formation of the Barisan Nasional (National Front), a new alliance of

A methane gas plant on Labuan Island. Labuan, off the Borneo coast near the Sarawak-Sabah border but administered directly from Kuala Lumpur, is being developed rapidly as an industrial center. Photo by Nick Seward/*Far Eastern Economic Review*

The king of Malaysia is elected for a five-year term by and from among the country's nine sultans. His portrait appears on Malaysia's currency.

nine ethnic parties, including UMNO, MCA, MIC, PAS, and several parties based in Sarawak and Sabah. The Barisan Nasional survived Razak's death in 1976 and maintained its dominant position in politics until the administration of Malaysia's current prime minister, Mahathir bin Mohamad.

Mahathir was elected chairman of UMNO in 1981 in a close intra-party contest with his perennial rival, Tungku Razaleigh Hamzah. In the national elections of 1982, the UMNO-dominated Barisan Nasional won a clear majority of the seats in parliament, but in the process it began to break apart over the issue of Islam. UMNO was challenged within the Barisan Nasional by the PAS, and in response moved to show itself to the electorate as Malaysia's truest and most effective protector of Islam. The political strategy of "out-Islaming" the PAS has worked for Mahathir, but at the cost of dividing the Malay electorate between UMNO and the PAS, and of shattering the unity of the Barisan Na-sional.

In 1988, Razaleigh and some of his allies broke with UMNO and founded a new party, Semangat '46 ("Spirit of 1946"), designed to serve as the spearhead of a united opposition coalition (including PAS and the Democratic Action Party), rivaling the Barisan Nasional. The national elections of October 1990 were therefore the first in Malaysia's history to feature strong, direct competition between ruling and opposition coalitions. The outcome was a personal triumph for Prime Minister Mahathir bin Mohamad; despite local losses in Penang, Kelantan, and Sabah, the Barisan Nasional, led by a reorganized UMNO, was returned to power with two thirds of the seats in parliament.

Electoral politics in Malaysia remains, as it has been from the beginning, a tangled web of ethnic, religious, and regional parties and alliances in which compromise and coalition building are the only possible keys to a prime minister's survival. Nevertheless, Malaysia must be regarded as an unqualified political success among the world's new nations. Except for Japan, it is the only country in East or Southeast Asia to have regularly held free, multiparty elections in the post-World War II period and to have survived shifts in political control without military intervention. That legacy is a fitting tribute to the architects of Malaysian independence.

Islam and Identity

Malaysia has sometimes been called a country without a culture. That is unfair; but it is certainly true to say that Malaysia is a country in search of a culture. It is a nation of many cultures that often exist in surprising isolation from each other, within the boundaries of a single country. But it lacks a single, unifying national culture within which all Malaysians can find a sense of national identity.

On the level of everyday life, there are of course many cultural elements shared by all Malaysians, cutting across the ethnic boundaries of the "plural society." An atmosphere of relaxed sociability, exemplified especially by a fondness for sharing Malaysia's diverse cuisines with friends; a gregarious amiability and a dislike of friction, discord, or other kinds of social unpleasantness; a concern for friendship and family values; even an appreciation for the modern Western-influenced popular culture of cars, rock music, and blue jeans: all of these are elements of a national culture with which all Malaysians can feel comfortable.

Beyond that, however, many Malaysians (especially educated Malays) feel acutely the need for an "official" national culture, but the effort to find or create one has been difficult and frustrating. The fundamental problem, which appears to have no real solution, is that the politically dominant Malays insist that Malaysian national culture must be based above all on Islam, while that is the one proposition Malaysia's non-Muslims feel they cannot accept.

Islam and the Dakwah Movement

Part of the problem of Malaysian national identity lies in the nature of Malaysian Islam itself. As was shown in Chapter IV, Islam arrived in Malaya as an Indian religion. Traditionally, Malayan Islam was a generous and tolerant religion. Most Malays saw no contradiction between embracing the faith of the Prophet and retaining much of their older culture in their music, in their marriage ceremonies, even in their veneration of ancient gods of the rice fields and the mountains. (The situation was not the same everywhere in the East Indies. Brunei, for example, adopted a stricter and more orthodox Islam early on, and today is spared the anguish of coming to terms with modern Islamic fundamentalism.)

Since independence, however, the easygoing Islam of earlier generations has seemed to many Malays, especially young people, to be unable to protect them very well from the bewildering new challenges of modernization and Westernization. Both the wrenching insecurity felt by many Malays in the face of Chinese economic success and the material-

Running Amok

Amok is one of the very few Malay words to have entered the English language (others are *ketchup* and *sarong*). That the word was borrowed into English is not surprising, for the behavior that it describes made a strong impression on European visitors to Malaya. A person who "ran amok" would become frenzied and enraged, and would run through the streets of his village slashing at everyone he met with a *kris* or a machetelike *parang*, killing as many as possible. Ultimately, he would be surrounded and killed by his neighbors, both as on-the-spot punishment for his crime and because he was considered too dangerous to try to capture. One anthropologist has described running amok as "a public form of suicide."

Running amok was never commonplace in Malay society, but neither was it rare. What could explain such behavior? Most cultural anthropologists who have considered the matter agree that it is a reaction to the tightly knit and generally extremely peaceful nature of traditional Malay society. Life in a traditional *kampung* was (and is) lived in the constant presence of family members and neighbors; privacy was virtually unknown, both as a concept and in

ism of modern life, and Malay anxieties about the "immorality" of Western-derived popular culture often find expression in an escape into orthodox Islam. As the well-known author V. S. Naipaul explains,

> Malaysia is rich. Money, going down, has created a whole educated genera-
> tion of village people and drawn them into the civilization that once appeared
> to be only on the outer edge of darkness but is now universal.

practice. Decisions about all matters of importance were reached by consensus among all members of the community, with deference shown to the opinions of the old, the well-born, and the wealthy. Open disputes were frowned upon, and any display of anger met with instant disapproval. People were expected to be calm, reasonable, and community minded, and to avoid doing anything, by word or deed, that led to interpersonal disharmony or psychological distress.

Under those circumstances, anyone with a persistent problem, such as an unhappy marriage, jealousy, or an unreconcilable dispute with a neighbor, had almost no way of venting his anger safely. Instead, he would repress it; and if the problem was too strong to repress, after a while it might emerge in an explosion of murderous rage—running amok. (Running amok was almost entirely a male phenomenon; women expressed extremes of anger and frustration in other ways, such as outbursts of weeping or psychologically induced illness.) Running amok would have a tragic but socially understandable result; the angry person would inflict his anger on the community, and purge it by accepting his own death. After a period of sorrow and introspection, the community would return to its accustomed life of calm, cooperation, and consensus.

These young people do not always like what they find. Some have studied abroad, done technical subjects; but not many of them really know where they have been. In Australia, England, or the United States they still look for the manners and customs of home; their time abroad sours them, throws them back more deeply into themselves. They cannot go back to the village. They are young, but the life of their childhood has changed. . . .

The men of the villages, who feel they have already lost so much, find their path blocked at every turn. Money, development, education have awakened them only to the knowledge that the world is not like their village, that the world is not their own. Their rage . . . is comprehensive. Now they have a weapon: Islam. It is their way of getting even with the world. It serves their grief, their feelings of inadequacy, their social rage and racial hate.*

The adoption of fundamentalist Islam by these young people is not simply a matter of personal choice and personal faith. Rather, it involves participation in a movement aimed, first, at "purifying" Malaysian Islam, and second, at imposing Islamic values on all Malaysians. The first of those aims is the most important for most participants in the orthodox *dakwah* movement (the name is derived from a Malay word meaning "to call"), but the second is also embraced by many, and it has disturbing implications for the future of Malaysian culture and society.

The paramount goal of the *dakwah* movement is to encourage Malays to practice Islam strictly, and to purge Malay society of unorthodox practices. So, for example, *dakwah* adherents remind their fellow Malays to pray five times daily, to eat only *halal* (ritually clean) meat, to wear "Islamic clothing," to abstain from alcohol, and so on. Beyond that, they urge Muslims to avoid non-Muslim practices at weddings and other ceremonies, to abstain from listening to Western music, and in general to refrain from anything that might distract them from a pure religious life.

As a trend that is particularly strong among young people, the *dakwah* movement has often relied on peer pressure to achieve its goals. For example, Malay college women who prefer to dress in Western-style clothes have complained of being harassed by fundamentalist Muslim fellow students who call them "whores" for dressing immodestly. Malay restaurants that serve non*halal* meat have sometimes been invaded by

---

*V. S. Naipaul, *Among the Believers: An Islamic Journey.* New York: Vintage Books, 1982, p. 227.

The National Mosque, Kuala Lumpur. Islam is by law the national religion of Malaysia, and most Malays feel that Islam should also form the basis of national culture.

groups of *dakwah* students who demonstrate noisily and drive customers away. *Dakwah* groups have even invited Muslim missionaries from Pakistan to preach in Malaysia—not to non-Muslims, but to Malays who are lax in their religious practices.

As is true of members of fundamentalist religious groups in many parts of the world, participants in the *dakwah* movement say that they feel liberated by their religious orthodoxy, because it frees them from the confusion, distractions, and temptations of modern life. Yet for those who disagree, the pressure to conform to fundamentalist values can be very uncomfortable.

More ominously, some extremist groups within the *dakwah* movement have taken an aggressive and even violent approach to the movement's second goal, the spread of Islamic values throughout Malaysian society, Muslim and non-Muslim alike. In 1982 a group of Muslim students invaded a Hindu temple, wrecking religious images and scattering offerings on the floor. The people involved were arrested and prosecuted, but the ill feeling that the incident had created endured. Participants in Chinese festivals have occasionally been spat upon by Muslim fanatics who regard the Chinese as "unclean" because they eat pork.

These are isolated incidents, but the more general pressure to enact Islamic values into national law has resulted in systematic legal discrimination against Malaysia's non-Muslims. Political leaders seem to feel it necessary to adopt a position that says, in effect, "I'm a better Muslim than my opponents," and so religiously motivated legislation gains wide support within the government. For example, Malaysian law makes it easy for anyone to convert to Islam, but virtually impossible for a Muslim to convert to any other religion. Criticism of Islam is illegal; so are sexual relations between Muslims and non-Muslims. Officials have virtually arbitrary power to ban any practice of the non-Muslim community on the grounds that it is "un-Malaysian." Nor is conversion to Islam enough to win acceptance for non-Malays; Muslim Chinese and Indians are still discriminated against by affirmative-action laws.

And so the problem of Malaysian national culture truly does seem to be insoluble, at least in any terms that would be acceptable to the Malay ruling elite. The *dakwah* movement has a powerful appeal for most Malays. They see it as an affirmation of their own identity, which they feel should be the basis for Malaysian national identity. Yet every move to impose Islamic values on non-Muslims provokes resentment and discord. The results can be seen on every city street in the country.

Dress and Identity

To wear clothes is to proclaim who you are and what you believe. That fact, true everywhere in the world, is of particular importance in

Malaysia, where clothing provides an instantly recognizable sign of a person's ethnic identity and religious beliefs.

Traditional Malay dress for both men and women was based on a simple rectangle of *batik* cloth, wrapped and worn as a skirt (the style of wrapping was different for men and women). Women wore a long blouse called a *kebaya*, while men traditionally went shirtless but wore an elaborately tied headcloth. This outfit is still common in the *kampung*s of rural Malaysia, though today many men omit the headcloth and wear Western-style shirts or T-shirts.

Traditional dress for men of the upper classes was quite splendid, consisting of a wrapped *batik* skirt, a high-collared tunic based on the court costume of northern India, an elaborate headcloth, and a *kris*.

Advertisement for school uniforms, Melaka. All schoolchildren in Malaysia and Brunei wear a uniform of some kind. In Brunei, and at Malay religious schools in Malaysia, the standard short uniform skirt and blouse for girls shown here is replaced by an Islamic hijab.

Batik *and* Ikat

Cloth may seem to most Westerners to be merely a useful product with no special significance or importance, but it is a crucial aspect of culture in the Malay world. On the Malay Peninsula, in Borneo, and throughout the islands of Indonesia (and even, to a lesser extent, in the Philippines), the weaving and decoration of cloth, and the ownership, wearing, display, and exchange of fabrics, has deep significance. The prestige and cultural importance of cloth in the Malay world may perhaps be related to the large role played by woven goods, from mats to baskets to fabrics, in the rise of Southeast Asian civilization.

Two types of cloth in particular, *batik* and *ikat*, are of special interest in understanding the culture of the Malay world. Both are indigenous to that world, but they have very different cultural meanings. *Batik* is the fabric of the aristocratic, urban, and agricultural Malay peoples, while *ikat* belongs to the culture of the longhouse, the riverbank, and the forest.

Batik is a kind of dyed cotton cloth, decorated with a variant of the technique known as wax-resist dyeing. To a plain piece of cotton cloth, skilled workers (almost always women) apply patterns of melted beeswax with an implement that looks like an overgrown fountain pen. The cloth is then dipped in a dyebath; the areas covered with wax resist the dye, while the unwaxed portions are dyed the desired color. The wax is then boiled out of the cloth, and a new wax pattern is applied; the cloth is then dipped in a second

Section of an unusually fine piece of batik *cloth (nineteenth century), showing both the exquisite sense of design and the superior workmanship that characterizes this distinctively Malay art at its best.*

dyebath of a different color. The process continues with further cycles of waxing and dyeing until a complex pattern has been completed. A cheaper form of *batik* is made by block-printing the wax patterns with metal stamps dipped in melted wax; that work is usually done by men, because of the heavy labor involved.

Batik patterns are often handed down from mother to daughter; different regions, even different towns and villages, have their own characteristic patterns. But a length of *batik* cloth—a *kain batik* (often, but incorrectly, known by Westerners as a *sarong*)—worn as a wrapped skirt was the standard article of dress for both men and women in villages, towns, and aristocratic courts throughout the Malay-culture area. In premodern times people were by no means free to wear whatever pattern of *batik* they wanted. Some patterns were produced for the exclusive use of sultans and their families, other patterns for other members of the aristocracy; any commoner who dared to wear such patterns was severely punished.

Regardless of the pattern, however, those who wore *batik* thereby immediately distinguished themselves from the tribal peoples of the forests, rivers, and mountains who wore *ikat* cloth. *Ikat* is also made by a resist-dyeing technique, but instead of being dyed onto finished cloth, the pattern is created before the cloth is woven. To produce *ikat* cloth, the weaver (invariably a woman) would lay out the warp (that is, lengthwise) threads that she would later string on her loom, measuring their length and number precisely. Sections of warp thread would then be wrapped in bark tied tightly with string, creating portions of thread that were so tightly bound that dye could not penetrate into them. When all of the wrapping was completed, the threads would be dyed. The process might be repeated several times with dyes of different colors. The warp threads were then strung on the loom and woven with weft (crosswise) threads; as the cloth was woven, the pattern pre-dyed into the warp threads would emerge.

Patterns of *ikat* were specific to certain tribes and even to certain longhouses; individual patterns were passed down from generation to generation. *Ikat* fabrics of different sizes might be sewn into tubular skirts (true *sarongs*), or worn as headcloths or shoulder cloths. Some fabrics were intended primarily to be kept as a form of wealth, to be displayed on ritual occasions. Wedding ceremonies among the Iban required that heirloom cloths be exchanged between the families of the bride and groom; as one young woman told an anthropologist recently, "Without cloths, how could we marry?"

Today, *batik* is produced in Malaysia both as a fine art and on a semi-industrial basis; there is even, nowadays, cheap imitation *batik* of printed cotton or rayon (though that is spurned as inferior by all but the poorest village women). *Ikat*, too, is still produced in traditional fashion on simple looms in forest longhouses. Recently the Malaysian Ministry of Culture organized an intertribal competition for the weavers of the finest traditional *ikat* cloth. Pieces of fine antique *batik* and *ikat* are avidly collected by folk-art enthusiasts around the world. But on the level of everyday life, *batik* and *ikat* continue to be produced to be worn and displayed. In the Malay scheme of things, these two types of cloth symbolize as nothing else can the two worlds of village and tribe that coexist within the greater Malay world.

Children on their way home from school in Kuala Terengganu, West Malaysia. The girl wears the hijab, *the recently adopted dress of Malayan orthodox Islam.*

Before independence, the royal courts of the sultans issued detailed regulations about who could wear what kinds of clothing; for example, the wearing of yellow clothing was (and still is) restricted to members of royal families.

In Malaysia's large cities, most people—and virtually all middle-class professional people—wear Western clothes. As a concession to tropical heat, few men wear suits; the standard business outfit is a white shirt with dark trousers, while women wear Western dresses. Working-class men wear trousers and Western-style shirts or T-shirts. Women of the same class wear dresses or the traditional clothing of their own ethnic group. Wearing "ordinary" Western clothing is common to urban Malaysians regardless of ethnic group, but it is by no means a neutral choice. Rather, it says that the person who wears such clothing accepts, to some degree, Western values, modern business practices, and an international outlook. In Malaysia, to wear Western clothing is to distance one's self both from the *kampung* and from religious orthodoxy.

Yet many Malay men who wear Western clothes also make a gesture of religious identification by wearing a brimless black hat, the *songkok*, which is seen as both a badge of Malaysian nationalism and Islamic faith. Men who have gone on the *hajj*, the religious pilgrimage to Mecca, wear a white *songkok* instead. Fewer urban Malay men—and very few in the professional class—wear full "Islamic" dress, which consists of a white skirtlike lower garment and a long, flowing white shirt that reaches to the knees. "Islamic" dress is becoming much more common among urban Malay women of all classes, however. This costume, called the *hijab*, consists of a very full long skirt topped by a voluminous tunic; the head is covered by a large scarf that is wrapped under the chin, covering both the hair and the neck.

This garment is not traditionally Malay, nor is it Islamic in the sense of being prescribed by the Koran or by Muslim tradition. Rather it is a modern Arab fashion that originated in the cities of the Middle East as a compromise between "immodest" Western clothing and the full-scale veils worn by traditional Arab women. But the *hijab* has been adopted by Islamic orthodox movements throughout the world as a model of what religious women should wear, and it is enthusiastically promoted as a "Malaysian national dress" by the *dakwah* movement.

The *hijab* is also nearly universally worn by women in Brunei, where men customarily wear Western shirts and trousers with a *songkok*.

The most popular fashion for urban young people is T-shirts with slogans in English, worn with trousers or skirts or, for both sexes, jeans. These English-language T-shirts are often made in Malaysia, and while they follow international fads, their phrasing is sometimes amusingly eccentric (such as "Hello! Loving You Always"). Some teenagers wear deliberately outrageous clothes. There are Heavy Metal types in metal-studded leather trousers and jackets, with long frizzy hair; "mosquito riders," who roar around loudly on motorcycles late at night dressed in dirty denim; and Chinese dandies who imitate the latest high fashions from Hong Kong. All these styles are, of course, designed to provoke older people, and it works. As Prime Minister Mahathir once wrote, "Just as copying proper attire once led to the East adopting Western values regarding discipline, copying improper attire has infected the East with the values behind the Western change in attire."

In the cities, then, the choice of whether to wear Western clothes or Islamic dress proclaims the choice that a person has made between the values associated with modernization and the values associated with religious orthodoxy. Similarly, in the more heavily Malay and conservative countryside, the choice between the *kain batik* and the *hijab* represents a choice between the relaxed Islam traditional to Malaya and the fundamentalism of the *dakwah* movement.

Most Chinese Malaysians wear Western clothing, but many older Chinese prefer the loose, pajamalike black outfit worn by both men and women, especially among the working classes. The preference of young, urban Chinese women for high-fashion clothing, including short skirts, is looked upon by orthodox Muslims with horror as a sign of gross immodesty; for the women themselves, it is a strong sign (if an unconscious one) of contempt for the Malay effort to impose Islamic values on all of Malaysian society. Few young Chinese women now wear the tight-fitting, high-collared, slit-skirted *cheongsam* except for festive occasions, but it too is a badge of Chinese ethnic identity.

Rural Malaysian Indians commonly wear Indian dress: for men the *dhoti*, a wrapped white skirt worn either without a shirt or with a white

This young Chinese mother's miniskirt contrasts sharply with the ultramodest religious dress now worn by many Malay women.

tunic, and for women the *sari*, a flowing silk or cotton wrapped dress worn over a short, tight-fitting blouse. In the cities, most Indian men wear Western clothing; many urban women wear *sari*s, though those women with office jobs wear Western dresses.

In Borneo, where forest-dwelling longhouse peoples are typically fairly poor, most men wear ordinary Western work clothes, and women wear cheap Western-style dresses. But some women still customarily wear traditional clothes, a tubular *ikat* sarong and a wrapped breast cloth; at festivals, men also wear *ikat* loincloths and shoulder cloths, along with elaborate headdresses. Among politically active Iban, Kayan, Kenyah, and other forest peoples, the wearing of native dress has become a sign of rejection of Peninsular Malay values and, in some cases, of participation in the environmental preservation movement.

Street scene in an Indian neighborhood of downtown Kuala Lumpur. The dhoti *worn by the old man in the center marks him as being most likely a rural visitor to the big city.*

Detail of an Iban ikat *cloth from the Skrang River, Sarawak. The central design, woven from predyed cotton thread, represents a stylized water monster.*

"You are what you eat," says the Western proverb. In Malaysia, it is more true to say that you are what you wear. The diversity of clothing worn by Malaysians of every description is a vivid sign of how far Malaysia remains from having a single national culture.

Culture and the Arts

Throughout the Malay world, a basic but unspoken principle of living is that life should be beautiful. What in the West would be called "folk art" is not called art at all in the Malay world; people simply make their ceremonies, habits, and objects of daily use as beautiful as possible because life is better that way. A pack basket, for example, used for carrying things to and from the fields, will be woven with elaborate patterns of differently colored bamboo strips—not because it makes it more useful, but because it makes it more pleasing. The same is true of things made purely for fun. Kites are elaborately painted in bright colors, tops are carved in fantastic patterns. Music, dance, and theatrical performances accompany every festive event, adding further to the enjoyment of life.

It is unfortunately true that traditional Malay culture has suffered badly from neglect and decline in recent decades. In striking contrast to Indonesia, for example, where traditional arts of all kinds remain quite strong, in Malaysia it is often even difficult to find people who remember the old dances, or to locate a puppeteer to perform a shadow-puppet play. Modernization and Westernization have distracted members of the elite from their own traditional culture, and the villages are neither vigorous nor traditional enough any more to carry on the old arts alone, without elite support. Islamic reformers, too, have sometimes been hostile to traditional culture, accusing it of contributing to lax religious attitudes.

On the other hand, the ethnic diversity that creates so many problems for Malaysia is also a source of great cultural richness. Malay, Chinese, Indian, and tribal cultures, each in their own ways, contribute to the nation's music, theater, art, and enjoyment of leisure, making Malaysia a kaleidoscope of cultural diversity.

Music and Dance

Malaysia shares with the greater Malay world (and with Thailand and Cambodia as well) a distinctive—and, to Western ears, often quite beautiful—musical tradition based on the *gamelan*. The *gamelan* is not the name of an instrument, but rather of an instrumental ensemble or orchestra containing drums, xylophones, metallophones (like xylophones, but with metal rather than wooden bars), and tuned gongs. In Malaysia, the *gamelan* also usually includes bamboo flutes and an ancient Arab version of the violin, called a *rebab*. A *gamelan* can be small or large, and its music can cover a wide range of styles, from slow and stately to sad and haunting to lively and cheerful. *Gamelan* music is played at all Malay festive and ceremonial occasions, whether as ensemble music purely for listening or as an accompaniment to dance.

Most modern Malay popular music closely resembles Western popular and rock music, which has been adopted in virtually every country on earth. But one very interesting type of modern music is a kind of compromise between the *gamelan* and Western music. Played by an ensemble of drums, tuned gongs, flutes, and an accordion, it has a distinctively Middle Eastern flavor but sometimes borrows melodies from Western popular songs. This type of music was extremely popular a generation or two ago, and is having a modest revival today. Some Malaysian rock groups have also developed a kind of "fusion rock" that includes elements of Western, Arabic, and traditional Malay musical forms.

Listening to the radio in any large city in Malaysia gives a quick and accurate impression of the country's cultural diversity. Over the course of a day, tuning in to several radio stations (all of which are government controlled), one might hear *gamelan* music accompanying a Malay soap opera; an Indian popular singer from Bombay; a performance of Chinese opera; Arab music accompanying an Islamic religious broadcast; Chinese rock music from Hong Kong; a Malaysian pop group; and even the latest rock band from England.

Traditional Malay dances, accompanied by *gamelan* music, are sometimes performed on festive occasions. They include ensemble dances for men, for women, and for men and women together (for example, in a traditional courtship dance); but mixed social dancing in the Western sense was unknown in traditional Malay society. Today it is found only among fairly sophisticated urban young people. Traditional dance is not often performed, however, and it is something of a dying art. At a recent performance of Malay dances in Kuala Lumpur, for example, it turned out that the dancers had been imported from Java—not enough were available locally. In addition to what might be called folk dance, there once was a kind of performance art that was based on Middle Eastern music and sometimes also included dance; called *ghazal*, it was designed to be performed by young women for the enjoyment of sultans and other members of the aristocracy. It has now disappeared almost entirely. In 1990, a delegation of dance experts from America, Europe, and Indonesia visited performing arts departments at several Malaysian universities to discuss how *ghazal* and other traditional dances might be revived.

Western modern dance also is known to some extent in Malaysia. In Kuala Lumpur a number of young choreographers have attempted—to critical praise, but relatively little popular support—to create a Malaysian modern dance that draws artistic inspiration from both Western and Malay sources.

Folk dance remains more vigorous among the various ethnic groups of northern Borneo. The Iban, for example, perform a number of dances—some for pure enjoyment, some with religious significance—to the accompaniment of a simple *gamelan* of drums and gongs. One of the most impressive is the hornbill dance, in which men wearing headdresses and arm ornaments of hornbill plumes turn and swoop in imitation of the flight of that majestic bird, which is considered sacred in traditional Iban religion. A century ago, the Ranee (Queen) of Sarawak described another dance, performed for her by the women of a longhouse:

It was slow, undulating, seductive, tender. As the dancers stood motionless before us, their draperies hung straight from their chins to their toes, their feet being hidden in the folds of their petticoats. When they slowly lifted their arms, an undulation wrinkled up the folds of their garments, as though a sigh, beginning at their heels, ran upwards and lost itself in the air above their heads. . . .

Theater

Malaysia's greatest theatrical tradition is the *wayang kulit* shadow-puppet play. Like many aspects of Malay culture, *wayang kulit* has

ancient roots, and is shared widely throughout Southeast Asia, from South China, Thailand, and Vietnam to the East Indies. Most critics agree that it has reached its highest development in Java; Malaysian *wayang kulit* resembles, and has been influenced by, the Javanese form.

Wayang kulit puppets are made of water-buffalo hide, stiffened by a central spine of buffalo horn. They have moveable arms manipulated by thin rods, also made of buffalo horn. Although the puppets are elaborately painted and gilded, in performance they are intended to be seen only as shadows cast by an oil lamp upon a screen of stretched cotton cloth; the leather puppets are pierced and carved in lacelike patterns to give contour and definition to their shadows. Performances are accompanied by a small *gamelan*. All the puppets are manipulated by a single puppeteer, called a *dalang*, who recites the narrative of the play and speaks the parts of each character. Traditionally, because the *dalang* seems to give a kind of temporary life to his inanimate puppets, he was expected also to be a man of pure moral character. The profession of *dalang* has high prestige and requires great skill. It also requires great stamina. Performances of *wayang kulit* generally begin in the late evening, and often go on all night.

Although *wayang kulit* theater is an integral part of Malay culture, Islam prohibits any depiction of the human form (the prohibition applies to animals as well). As a result, the themes of puppet plays are not drawn from Muslim sources, but rather from the older Indian roots of Malay tradition. Puppet plays are most often based on the great poetic epics of India, especially the *Ramayana* and the *Mahabharata*.

Another form of Malay drama is *makyong*, a popular theatrical form in which, to the accompaniment of *gamelan* music, actors and actresses sing, dance, and act out heroic tales of the sultans and princesses of

An Iban woman dances to the music of drums and gongs on the verandah of her village longhouse. She wears a sarong and breast cloth of ikat *cloth, and heavy silver jewelry.*

A Wayang Kulit Performance

The Mexican artist Miguel Covarrubias, who lived on the Indonesian island of Bali in the 1930's, wrote a description of the setting of a *wayang kulit* performance that could still apply to Malaysia today:

There are no announcements made when a wayang show is to take place. Somehow the rumor spreads from person to person and there is a crowd even before the dalang arrives. By the time he begins to stretch his screen, a great mob has gathered, sitting quietly on the ground, giving no signs of impatience at the customary endless wait for the play to begin. . . .

The dalang brings the marionettes out of the chest one by one, taking his time to introduce the characters. . . . On the right the dalang places the good and noble characters: the gods, kings, princes, princesses, and their attendants. On the left the evil characters are lined up: giants, demons, witches, and the villains of the play in general. . . .

The puppets are then removed, leaving the screen empty, and the play begins. It may be the episode from the Ramayana *in which the divine prince Rama tries to rescue Sita, his beloved bride, from the giant Rawana. . . . Here Rama is assisted by a great army of monkeys in terrific battles in which "they discharged so many arrows that they could not see each other any more." Millions of monkeys and* raksasas *[monsters] alike are slain before Rawana is killed and Sita rescued.*

Every object and every move of the [puppets] has a symbolic significance aside from the purely entertaining aspect of the show. The dalang is an artist and a great spiritual teacher. . . . He is invariably the star of the show.

(From Miguel Covarrubias, *Island of Bali.* New York: Alfred A. Knopf, 1936, 1937, pp. 237–240.)

olden times. Rather like Shakespearean comic characters, actors representing commoners provide humorous interludes between passages of high drama. As in *wayang kulit*, many of the themes of *makyong* are drawn from ancient Indian literature. In the state of Kelantan, a very ancient form of Thai-derived drama called *menora* is preserved, in which male actors (who play both male and female roles) perform in masks.

Another important theatrical tradition in Malaysia is Chinese opera (although, of course, it is rejected by Malays as "not part of Malaysian

A dalang *performing a* wayang kulit *shadow puppet play.*   Courtesy of the Malaysian National Museum, Kuala Lumpur.

culture"). Chinese opera is often called Beijing opera by Westerners, but that is partly a mistake, for there are many regional operatic traditions in China. Chinese opera in Malaysia is most likely to be Canton opera or Fujian opera. Despite regional differences, all Chinese opera features falsetto singing to the accompaniment of an orchestra of drums, gongs, cymbals, and wind instruments, gorgeous costumes and elaborate makeup, highly stereotyped acting (willowy and fragile for young women, stern for older men, fierce for villains, and so forth), and energetic, acrobatic dance interludes. The plays usually feature themes from Chinese history, and can be performed either by live actors or, in a puppet version, by marionettes.

Modern Western-style theater exists in Malaysia, but it faces many obstacles. Ian Buruma reports that a series of satirical sketches by the Malaysian Chinese writer Thor Kah Hoong was criticized as "un-Malaysian" by government censors. The Malay playwright Syed Alwi has given up writing for the stage, saying sadly, "Malaysian culture does not exist." And Malaysia's best-known director and theater critic, Krishin Jit, has also written pessimistically about the possibility of creating a truly Malaysian theatrical tradition.

Malaysian television production is generally uninspiring, being mostly a mix of variety shows, soap operas and costume dramas, and rather dull government-sponsored documentaries. This is hardly surprising, because the industry is small, is generally underfunded, and must produce programs that have little export potential and are limited to a relatively small national audience. Moreover, it must compete with imported programs from Indonesia, Hong Kong, the United States, and other countries, and also must accommodate itself to the strict demands

Backstage and center stage at a puppet performance of Chinese opera, in a temple courtyard in Melaka.

of government censorship. It would be remarkable if anyone could produce first-rate television programming under those circumstances.

The Malaysian film industry, too, is not terribly advanced; many of its products are situation comedies or costume dramas, broadly acted and rather poorly produced, modeled in style and content on Indian popular cinema. A few Malaysian film directors have managed to produce films of high quality that break with old stereotypes and reflect a genuinely Malaysian sensibility; but they, too, must contend with censorship, tight funding, and a small national audience.

Literature

Malaysia does not have a strong literary tradition. Because "high culture" in Malaya was almost always foreign culture, literature in premodern times generally meant literature in a foreign language—the Sanskrit classics of India, the Koran and other Arabic (and Persian) religious writings, or, for educated Malays under British colonial rule, English literature. But while Malayan culture has always drawn heavily on foreign influences, Malay writers (like other artists) have also continually adapted those influences to produce literature that is distinctively Malayan in character.

The oldest work of literature in the Malay language is *Sejara Melayu (Chronicle of Malaya)*, written in the early sixteenth century. A history of the kingdoms of the Malay Peninsula, with emphasis on Melaka, it is regarded as a literary masterpiece, and it provided a model of Malay prose for other writers down to the late nineteenth century. Yet relatively little literature in Malay was produced during that period; what there was consisted primarily of historical chronicles, religious works, and poetry. There undoubtedly were other works of literature from the nineteenth century and earlier that no longer exist; paper tends to deteriorate rapidly in Malaysia's tropical climate, and works that were produced in manuscript form but never printed might simply have disappeared.

The cultural confusion of modern Malaysia is reflected strikingly in the country's failure to develop a modern national literature. There are good Malay writers, but they are overshadowed by writers in Indonesia, where the population is ten times larger than that of Malaysia and Standard Malay is universally accepted as the national language. Malaysian Chinese and Indians have shown little interest in writing in Malay, or even in reading the works of Malay writers; and Malays have shown even less interest in reading literature written by their fellow Malaysians in Chinese or Tamil. Some Malaysian writers, like the poet Cecil Rajendra, attempt to sidestep the problem by writing exclusively in English. But that also does nothing to put them in the mainstream of Malaysian literature—the real problem is that the mainstream is hard to identify, and perhaps does not exist.

Visual Arts

The Islamic religious rule prohibiting the creation of any representation of living creatures, whether as paintings or sculpture, meant that "art" in the Western sense never developed in Malaysia, at least until modern times. Painting, carving, and metalwork were limited generally to the field of decorative art. Many types of traditional decorative art are dying out rapidly in urban Malaysian society, as members of the wealthy elite prefer to live in Western-style mansions rather than in more traditional houses.

In Malay culture, decorative art followed the lead of the Muslim world, employing patterns of foliage, abstract geometrical designs, and other nonrepresentational motifs to decorate palaces and other public buildings. Mosques, designed in Middle Eastern style with gilded domes and tall, slender minarets (towers from which the call to prayer is chanted five times each day), were often decorated with elaborately carved stonework. Most great buildings, however, whether palaces or mosques, depended less for their decoration on architectural detail than on beautiful fixtures and furnishings. Metalworkers, again following Middle Eastern models, created hammered and engraved bowls, trays, and other ornamental pieces for the use of the elite. Many of these were of brass or silver; the wealthiest sultans preferred pure gold. Personal articles, too, such as the handles and scabbards of *kris*es, snuffboxes, jewelry cases, and similar objects were beautifully crafted in silver or gold. The ready availability of tin made pewter (an alloy of tin and lead) a favorite metal for plates and other tableware, and even today Malaysia is a major producer of fine pewterware. Hangings and cushions of silk or *songket* cloth (cloth woven with gold threads), carved and gilt furniture, and carpets imported from Persia created an interior decor of comfort and luxury. Other artists, working for wealthy Muslim patrons, created luxury manuscript copies of the Koran, written in beautiful calligraphy with pages decorated with hand-colored floral and geometric designs; the books were bound in gem-studded silver or gilt bindings.

In the Chinese community, many decorative articles such as porcelain, lacquerware, and scroll paintings were normally imported from China. Local craftsmen, however, became well known for creating a distinctive "Straits Chinese" style of decorative art, notably in terracotta and tilework architectural details for the houses of the wealthy, and in carved and gilt wooden furniture. The latter was produced in Melaka and Penang, and exported widely throughout the East Indies.

Beginning in the late eighteenth century, a few Chinese commercial artists began to produce landscape paintings and portraits in oils or watercolors, intended for sale to foreign clients. Most of these artists were trained as assistants to a handful of English painters resident in the Straits Settlements who specialized in producing scenes of "exotic Malaya" for the foreign community or for sale back in England. Some of these Chinese assistants went on to become successful artists in their own right; their works are now highly prized by antique collectors.

Within the Indian community, art was employed primarily in the service of religion. Hindu temples typically are elaborately decorated with stone carvings and terra-cotta sculptures, inset tilework, and other colorful details. Indian painters produced hundreds of paintings, or, in more recent times, colored prints, of gods and goddesses for devotional use in home shrines.

Some of the most interesting and beautiful decorative art in Malaysia is that of the tribal cultures of northern Borneo. In the forest, where hardwoods and bamboo are readily available but metal and stone are scarce, many ordinary objects for use in daily life are carved from wood. Such things as knife handles, bowls, stools, and other utensils and furnishings are often carved with animal figures of great expressive force. Formerly weapons such as clubs and spears were especially carefully decorated, perhaps to impart to the weapons themselves some of the power of the animal figures that decorated them. Many other articles, such as baskets and mats, are made of woven bamboo. Using strips of bamboo dyed dark red or black along with those left undyed, such articles are often woven in complex and beautiful patterns.

The tribes of North Borneo made very little pottery, but pottery jars are nevertheless closely associated with longhouse life. For centuries, Chinese merchants brought with them to Borneo heavy pottery storage jars, some three or four feet high, decorated with designs of dragons, bamboo, and other Chinese motifs. These jars were an important item of trade, used to buy the beeswax, hornbill ivory, sandalwood, and other forest products that the Chinese merchants took back home. In longhouses throughout Borneo today, such jars remain in use to store rice, cooking oil, and other foodstuffs. Though they would be worth thousands of dollars on the antique market, they are not for sale, because they are treasured as family heirlooms.

Metalwork also played a significant role in the arts of northern Borneo. Women in the longhouse villages often wear heavy silver jewelry, which serves not only as a type of personal ornament but also as a convenient way of keeping the family's wealth in a compact and readily available form. In Brunei and other towns along the coast, members of the elite guarded their homes and ships with brass cannons that were often as good-looking as they were effective. Some, for example, were cast with muzzles that resembled dragons' or tigers' heads.

In contemporary Malaysia, a number of artists work in oils and watercolors to produce paintings influenced by Western art but distinctively Malaysian in subject matter and style. Some of these paintings are of mediocre quality, designed to be sold as tourist souvenirs, but there are some artists whose work is of a high standard. Some of Malaysia's most interesting painters work not on canvas or paper, but in the traditional medium of *batik*, using it to produce pictorial art rather than cloth intended to be worn as clothing.

Festivals

One of the great attractions of Malaysia for a foreign visitor is that there always seems to be a festival of some kind going on. And for a change, no one seems to worry about how these festivals fit into a "Malaysian national culture"; festivals tend to be celebrated *within* Malaysia's various ethnic communities. Outsiders are welcome to watch, and enjoy, but festivals are an occasion for celebrating one's own ethnic identity and solidarity.

The most widely celebrated festival in Malaysia, and in Brunei as well, is *Hari Raya Puasa*, a great feast that ends the Muslim month of Ramadan. Because the 354-day Muslim lunar calendar does not coincide with the 365-day solar calendar used in the West, the (Western calendar) date of this festival is different every year. Muslims throughout Malaysia celebrate the end of a month of fasting and penitence with a daylong party of music, eating, and general merrymaking. *Hari Raya Puasa* has become a sort of national festival in Malaysia, reaching out beyond the Muslim community itself. Chinese, Indians, Christians, and other non-Muslims enjoy the feasting and celebration of *Hari Raya Puasa* as much as Muslims do, and there is a great deal of visiting of friends across ethnic lines. The ethnic barriers of Malaysia's plural society are by no means absolute, and they break down easily on occasions of general happiness and good feeling.

Perhaps the most spectacular and colorful of Malaysia's annual festivals is *Deepavali*, the Hindu festival of lights, which is celebrated in October or November. During *Deepavali*, Hindu temples are decked with paper flowers, colorful offerings of food and cloth, and hundreds of votive oil lamps; their courtyards are thronged with worshippers. *Deepavali* is a time of renewal, and during the several days of the festival Indian shops are crowded with people buying new clothes for the occasion. Another important Indian holiday, particularly among Tamils, is *Thaipusam*, celebrated in late January or early February, which features colorful processions winding through the streets near temples of the god Subramaniam. Among the worshippers are men who show their devotion to the god by walking with their chests, arms, and legs pierced by thick steel spears weighted down with heavy iron weights; in a deep state of trance, they neither bleed nor feel pain.

Chinese festivals are also colorful and boisterous. The most important include Chinese New Year (in January or February), a week-long festivity of feasting, visiting temples and friends, and setting off thousands of firecrackers to drive away the woes of the past year. For some years in the 1970's and early 1980's, the Lion Dance, traditionally part of the New Year celebrations, was prohibited by the government as being "un-Malaysian," but in response to strenuous Chinese protests, it once again is allowed. *Qingming*, the Spring Festival, in April, and the Seventh Moon Festival, in August, are two other important Chinese holidays. The latter is primarily a family festival, a time to show reverence to the family's ancestors. On nearly any day of the year, one is likely to encounter a Chinese wedding or funeral, both occasions for colorful processions in the streets.

Brunei is a more strictly Muslim country even than Malaysia, and its Chinese population is smaller and less politically influential. For those reasons, Chinese festivals, although celebrated in Brunei, are generally more modest and subdued there.

In northern Borneo, the most interesting festivals are naturally those of Borneo's indigenous peoples. The Iban harvest festival, for example, features hornbill dances and colorful images of hornbill birds (made of woven bamboo and colored cloth) erected on tall poles in front of each longhouse. In Sabah, the Kadazans, although now overwhelmingly Christian, also celebrate a harvest festival that includes many rituals preserved from their pagan past.

In Malaysia, the grandest festival of all takes place once every five years, when a new king is enthroned. This is a truly national occasion, sponsored by the government and meaningful to all of the country's citizens. The new king is ushered into the throne room wearing a bejeweled high-collared uniform and a splendidly elaborate headcloth of *kain songket*, the aristocratic fabric woven with threads of gold. He wears a *kris* in a jewel-encrusted scabbard, a symbol of his royal authority; and he walks beneath a canopy of saffron-yellow parasols of state.

The clothing, regalia, and rituals of enthronement are links with the royal pageantry of the distant past, and draw deeply on the Hindu roots of Malay culture.

Sports and Recreation

Malaysia is a sports-mad nation. When Malaysia hosted the Southeast Asia Games in the summer of 1989, business throughout the country often ground to a halt as everyone watched important events on television. In daily life, large numbers of people regularly take part, as players or spectators, in both Western and traditional Malay sports and games.

The most popular sport in Malaysia, as in most of the world, is undoubtedly soccer. Semiprofessional teams attract large crowds for matches in major cities, and it seems that every small town has its own

The weekly market day in the town of Kota Belud, Sabah, is enlivened by a soccer match between two local teams.

amateur soccer club. And a common sight everywhere in the country is a group of children kicking a soccer ball around a schoolyard, or standing in a circle practicing headers.

Perhaps one reason why soccer holds a particular fascination for Malays is that it resembles the old native game of *sepak takraw*, or kickball. *Sepak takraw* is played with a woven rattan ball, which must be kept in the air as it is kicked around by a group of players standing in a circle. A point is lost whenever the ball touches the ground. A variant of *sepak takraw* is played across a net, rather like volleyball played with the feet.

Two other extremely popular Western sports also are played over a net. Badminton is a national passion in Malaysia, but it is a far cry from the gentle and good-natured game played in American backyards. Malaysian badminton is played for keeps, a vigorously athletic game of high lobs and slashing volleys. Top Malaysian players are usually among the contenders for the world championship in badminton, and Malaysia has several times won the Thomas Cup, symbol of world badminton team supremacy. Volleyball also is among the country's most popular games, both for casual recreation and in organized competition.

Two other Western sports that have become very popular in Malaysia are basketball and field hockey; the latter is widely played by school and university teams. Basketball is especially popular in the Chinese community, but, as is true in many parts of the world, sports of all kinds in Malaysia tend to cross ethnic barriers with ease. Team sports in Malaysia tend to be multiethnic both for participants and for spectators; this is emphatically true of semiprofessional and national teams, where skill, not ethnic identity, is the overriding concern.

A reflection of the British colonial heritage, cricket has an enthusiastic, if limited, following in Malaysia. As in England, this distant cousin of baseball is especially favored by the educated elite, and it is a standard feature of the physical-education programs in upper-class private schools.

Kite flying is a popular recreation throughout the Malay world. Taking advantage of steady sea breezes, people in coastal villages enjoy flying enormous kites (some as much as twelve feet long and ten feet broad) made of lacquered cloth stretched on bamboo frames. The largest kites exert a powerful pull, and can be flown only by teams of strong men; daring small children sometimes climb up the kitestring and drop off into the surf. Kites are flown mainly for the fun of it, but sometimes competitions are organized to see which team can fly its kite highest.

Another distinctive Malay pastime is top spinning. Especially in the northeastern peninsular states of Kelantan and Terengganu, and particularly on festival days, people enjoy spinning large wooden tops, some as big as dinner plates and weighing as much as ten pounds. Beautifully made and perfectly balanced, these tops can spin for hours; naturally, the person whose top spins the longest wins. There is also a game of "top fighting," in which one person uses his top to try to knock his opponent's top out of a circle (rather like a giant game of marbles).

Malay martial arts, *silat*, have enjoyed a revival in popularity in recent years, possibly under the influence of the Hong Kong *kung-fu* movies that attract avid audiences throughout Malaysia. Said to have been developed by the bodyguards of sultans in ancient times, *silat* is a type of unarmed combat featuring slashing blows and kicks delivered from a deep crouching position. *Silat* is now widely taught in martial-arts academies as a form of physical training and as a competitive sport.

Daily Life

It is not possible here to describe comprehensively the daily life of all of Malaysia's people, given the country's ethnic and regional diversity. Instead, in this chapter we will present a series of portraits of individual Malaysians of different ages, ethnic groups, regions, and walks of life, in an attempt to suggest how many people conduct their daily lives. All the people described below are fictional, but they are not entirely imaginary; their portraits are based on written sources and the author's conversations and personal observations in Malaysia and Brunei.

A Chinese Grandfather

Wong Jin Han retired a few years ago from the day-to-day business of his wholesale rattan furniture company in Melaka. He still looks in at the office every day; after all, it is on the ground floor of his own house, with the workshops and warehouse in the rear. But his eldest son runs the business now, and Mr. Wong is content to let him do it. Many things have changed, and he is glad not to have to worry about them. It is hard to get Malaysian rattan now that so much of the forest has been logged over; his son has to rely on the Indonesian smugglers who bring raw rattan across the Strait of Malacca from Sumatra in their old wooden boats. That means the price has gone up and the supply is irregular; sometimes orders for furniture cannot be filled on time, which makes the customers unhappy. But somehow his son seems able to cope with it, using his new computer to keep track of everything. To Mr. Wong, it is all very mysterious.

So it is best for him only to visit the office for a little while in the morning, not to interfere. He enjoys his free time. He is a respected man in the community who has given large donations to his local Chinese temple; his neighbors look up to him. Sometimes during the day he likes to walk over to the Benevolent Society hall next to the temple and play mah-jongg with his other retired friends. But his son doesn't like him to lose too much money gambling, so often he just stays at home, taking care of his pet birds, tending his potted flowers, and playing with his beloved grandchildren.

Mr. Wong leads a comfortable and contented life. His wife died several years ago, but his daughter-in-law is a good, dutiful woman who always sees to it that he has everything he wants. His family has turned out well. His eldest son is a good businessman, and the youngest son is in medical school at the National University of Singapore; he will have a successful career. His only daughter got married last year to a promising young man who already is the office manager of a travel agency in the city. The wedding was very expensive, but he didn't mind that because now she is settled for life in a good family. Besides, it would have been unthinkable to risk losing face with his old friends by not giving his daughter a lavish wedding feast. He doesn't see her often,

A woman and her grandson head home from the outdoor market in a trishaw. Trishaws, bicycle-powered taxicabs, are the main means of short-distance public transportation in Malaysia's towns and small cities.

because her duty now is to her husband's family, and although he understands that, he misses having her around the house.

His only worry is about his middle son, who did not apply himself at school, and so was not able to get admitted to college—especially with the preference given to *bumiputra*s. So his son works as a cook on a Greek cruise ship somewhere on the other side of the world, and gets home only about once every three years. But he sends money every month, so Mr. Wong knows that he is a good son.

Mr. Wong's greatest satisfaction is thinking about his own funeral. It will be a grand affair, and he enjoys knowing that it will be talked about for months afterward. His red-lacquered coffin already is kept in a storeroom of the furniture workshop; he hopes he won't need it for many years yet, but it is a comfort to know that it is there. His gravesite, too, has already been chosen in consultation with the temple's fortune-teller. It is a good one, located just where land, wind, and water meet in the right way, so it will be sure to bring good luck to his descendants for many generations. His coffin will ride on a truck decorated with paper flowers, preceded by another truck carrying the orchestra from the local Chinese opera company. Behind it will walk his children and grandchildren, dressed in plain burlap mourning clothes. There will be many more trucks full of flowers sent by his friends, and a long line of cars bringing mourners to the cemetery. Afterward there will be a feast that people will remember—he has been saving for it for years. Now he can wait cheerfully for that grand event, and enjoy himself in the meantime.

A Brunei Housewife

Soraya Aziz is an ordinary housewife in Seria, Brunei, a city near the oilfields on the coast northwest of the capital. Her husband, like most men in the city, works for Brunei Shell, and he has a good job as a welder on the oil rigs. The only thing she doesn't like about his job is that when he works on an offshore platform, he sometimes is gone for a week at a time. But that is a small price to pay for the good living he provides for his family, and she does not complain.

Mrs. Aziz herself went only to elementary school, but she knows that her three children will have all the education they want. Her two daughters are in middle school, and her older son is in elementary school. The youngest son is only three; she could send him to a nursery school, but prefers to keep him at home. Recently the government opened two new schools in the city, so now her children can go to separate girls' and boys' schools, instead of having to study in the same building. Mrs. Aziz approves very strongly of that; she is a very religious woman.

When her husband is away on his job, several of her woman friends often come over to her house for the afternoon; the young children play together while the women drink coffee and chat. When she goes shopping, a neighbor often joins her. It is more proper that way; she wants no one to be able to accuse her of talking to a strange man alone. The stores are well stocked with everything she wants, and the open-air market provides fresh fruit and vegetables daily. Naturally she always wears a *hijab*. It sometimes is uncomfortable in the heat of the coastal tropics, but her house and car are air-conditioned, so it's no bother.

Mrs. Aziz is careful to give her husband no occasion to complain about her, so she tries to be careful with money, but she does love to shop. Especially she loves to indulge her passion for jewelry. Whenever she has saved enough from her household accounts, she goes to the gold shop to buy another piece. When she walks in her flowing *hijab*, she can hear the clinking of the many gold bracelets she wears on each wrist, and there are plenty of gold chains around her neck, hidden beneath her head scarf. The greatest treat of her life was when her husband took her to Singapore for a week several years ago. When a visitor asks what she did, she giggles and replies, "I shopped."

Mrs. Aziz knows nothing about politics; that is, she says firmly, men's business. Lowering her voice, she whispers that she doesn't like the rumors she hears about how the sultan loves to gamble in casinos when he visits Europe. But she shakes off that thought quickly; the government, she insists, has been very good to her. Last year her father was very ill with kidney failure, and nearly died. When it became clear that the medication he was taking was not working, a Brunei Shell medical-evacuation helicopter flew him to a hospital in Bandar Seri Begawan for

A Malay house near Melaka. Typical in architectural style but larger and more prosperous-looking than most, this house is built on stilts to provide coolness and protection from floods. The eaves of the roof project far beyond the walls of the house, providing shade throughout the day.

an operation, and except for incidentals, none of it cost the family a cent.

Mrs. Aziz has read about something called "women's liberation," but she think it is all nonsense. Such women, she says, must make very bad wives. She wants nothing to do with such talk. Her life is secure, comfortable, and predictable; there is nothing more she could want. Except, perhaps, another gold chain.

A Rubber-Estate Child

Seven-year-old Dreepa Narumandra lives on a rubber "estate" (plantation) not far from Kuantan on the east coast of the Malay Peninsula, but she has never been to the city. Her parents are both rubber workers

Malaysian Food

Malaysian food is as diverse as the peoples of Malaysia; it includes Malay, Chinese, and Indian cuisines, and many dishes that combine elements of two or more styles of cooking. The various ethnic groups of North Borneo also have their own distinctive dishes, though most of their food tends to be fairly simple "home cooking." The variety and tastiness of Malaysian food makes eating a favorite activity of visitors to the country.

Malay food is based on rice, seafood, hot chili peppers, and coconut cream (made from the soft meat of unripe coconuts). *Nasi lemak*, for example, is rice cooked in coconut cream and served with side dishes such as prawns cooked with hot peppers, dried anchovies, or sliced cucumbers. *Laksa* is a fish soup with noodles and sliced fresh chili peppers, flavored with coconut cream. *Satay*, the Malay dish best known outside Malaysia, is small pieces of meat (usually chicken, beef, or mutton) on a bamboo skewer, grilled and served with a sauce of ground-up peanuts and hot peppers; it is almost always accompanied by *ketupat*, rice dumplings cooked in bamboo leaves.

Chinese food in Malaysia is in general similar to Chinese food everywhere in the world; common dishes include *nasi goreng*, fried rice; *mee goreng*, fried noodles; and *lumpia*, overstuffed egg rolls. The best Chinese food in Malaysia is the Baba-Nyonya cuisine of Melaka and other towns on the west coast of the Peninsula. A simple but delicious Baba-Nyonya meal might begin with Chinese *dim sum* appetizers, continue with *nasi campur* (mixed rice; that is, white rice served with side dishes such as chili-fried prawns, dry-cooked spiced beef, fresh fish, curried eggs, and stir-fried vegetables) and end with a clear fish soup with bean-thread noodles. Some Baba-Nyonya dishes even include elements of Portuguese and Indian cooking. A good example is curry devil, chicken and potatoes cooked in a sauce flavored with shallots, garlic, chili peppers, lemon grass, and galingale root.

Every decent-sized town in Malaysia has at least one Indian restaurant, and every open-air market has a few Indian food stalls to provide refreshment for shoppers. Favorite Indian dishes in Malaysia include *roti canai*, thin pancakes dipped in a dish of curry sauce, and *murtabak*, pancakes stuffed with mutton and onion curry.

The enjoyment of food is recognized as one of life's great pleasures by Malaysians of every ethnic group, and people do not by any means confine themselves to the food of their own group. Especially in the cities, members of the sophisticated middle class enjoy eating every type of cuisine found in Malaysia, and European food as well. Chinese and Indians in particular often eat Malay food, and some secular Malays will even eat Chinese food—though that is no longer as common as it used to be. Because of peer pressure from more strictly orthodox Muslims, some cosmopolitan Malays who once would have thought nothing of eating Chinese dishes containing pork (or drinking alcohol, as well) now feel that it is better not to do so, at least in public. But for anyone not restrained by religious dietary laws, food in Malaysia offers a feast as diverse as it is delicious.

on the estate; she lives with them and her six brothers and sisters in a two-room house. Three other houses just like their own are attached as part of a single structure. The four families share an outhouse and a cook shed in the back yard.

Dreepa's father is a rubber tapper. Six days a week, he gets up at five in the morning to be able to start work at dawn, going out in a truck with other workers to the section of the estate that the foreman has decided to tap that day. He cuts a new groove in the bark of each tree, and makes sure that the coconut-shell cup in its wire holder is placed so that no latex will seep past it. After cutting bark until late morning, he and his fellow workers eat their noon meal among the trees and rest before going back to retrace their steps from the morning, emptying each cup into a large metal pail. At the end of the day, each worker's pail is weighed. Mr. Narumandra is paid M$8.75 (about US$3.25) per day if he collects a minimum of 24 pounds (11 kilograms) of latex, and a bonus if he gets more. After the pails are weighed and recorded, each worker empties the pail into a vat in the back of a truck, and the day's work is ended.

Mrs. Narumandra also works, but with seven children at home, she cannot be away for the entire day, so she is a part-time weeder. Usually she makes about M$3.00 per day. The family lives rent free in their house, and school and minimal medical care are free, so their wages are just enough to get by on. But they eat meat only twice a month, and the children's school uniforms were all bought secondhand and are kept carefully patched and mended.

The Narumandras are Tamils, like almost all their neighbors. Their family has worked on the rubber estate for three generations, and they see little hope that anything will change. Nor is it likely that they could get better jobs on the estate; the foremen are mostly better-educated Malayali Indians whose families came from Kerala on India's Malabar coast. Malayalis don't marry Tamils, and it is impossible to get a foreman's job without family connections.

Dreepa and a big crowd of estate children walk down the mile-long estate road early every morning to wait for the bus that takes them to school in the nearby town. Dreepa knows that her school doesn't look like the ones shown on television in the estate workers' recreation hall, but she doesn't realize quite how bad it really is. The desks are broken and shabby, and there are not enough of them, so some children have to sit two at a desk. The playground is a large patch of sun-baked dirt, laid out with a soccer field and a sagging badminton net. Worst of all, from her point of view, all the lessons are in Malay, which she seldom speaks in daily life. If there were money, she could go to a Tamil private school, but that is an impossible dream.

When Dreepa gets a little older, she will quit school to help her mother around the house. "Cultural attitudes remain," points out Irene Fernandez of the Malaysian Women's Development Collective. "If it's a matter of limited funds and choice, priority goes to the male." Perhaps Dreepa hopes that when she is old enough to marry, she will be able to leave the estate for a new life in a town. "For girls, marriage seems the only escape," says Fernandez, "but they later realize that this does not solve the problem." Unless she is exceptionally lucky, Dreepa will have nothing to look forward to but a life of hardship and poverty.

A Kuala Lumpur White-Collar Worker

Muhamed Halim is an accountant for a Japanese-owned company in Kuala Lumpur. He is thirty years old, and has worked for this firm since he graduated from Malaysian National University. He has quite a good job, but he sometimes feels uncomfortable in his office. The office manager, Mr. Fujimori, is Japanese, and all the workers are afraid of him. His Malay is not very good, and he always seems to be in a hurry. Mr. Fujimori doesn't seem to like being stationed in Malaysia, and maybe he takes out his resentment on his workers by being grumpy most of the time. Most of Mr. Halim's coworkers are Chinese, and he has little in common with them. They all seem to speak English better than he does, and he is sure Mr. Fujimori prefers Chinese to Malays. Even worse, they always smell of garlic and pork.

For Muhamed Halim, the worst problem is that it is hard to be a good Muslim working in such an office. If he wore proper Islamic clothing to work, Mr. Fujimori wouldn't stand for it; everyone has to come to work in a white shirt and dark trousers. He compromises as best he can, by wearing his black *songkok* hat to and from work and taking it off only when he reaches his office building. But at least his wife is always properly dressed. She comes from a small town in Perak, and she is a good, simple woman from a religious family.

The Halims live in an apartment in a new development north of the city. It means that Mr. Halim has a long bus ride to work every day, but it is the best they can afford right now. Someday, if he gets a promotion, he will be able to buy a small house. Right now, his main priority is to save money for his young son's circumcision ceremony. It needn't be held for a few more years, but the cost will be very heavy; the feast will be expensive, and he wants to have good musicians for the party. But worst of all, many relatives will arrive from the countryside, and it will be his responsibility to put all of them up in hotels for a week. Buying a house will have to wait.

Muhamed Halim is a solid and sober man now, but in his college years his behavior was rather daring. He even had a Chinese girlfriend for a while, and they would hold hands when they were away from other students. Of course, it was nothing serious; how could it be, when both families would have been outraged if they had gotten wind of it? But in his senior year at college, his life changed completely. He began going to an Islamic study group, part of the campus *dakwah* ministry, and he soon felt that living a religious life was the best way to find true happiness. He gave up drinking alcohol and eating non *halal* food, and did his best to pray at least once every day even if he couldn't always manage the prescribed five times. Gradually he dropped those of his friends who did not share his new feelings.

Muhamed Halim says that Islam makes him feel like a true Malaysian. It doesn't matter that the Chinese always seem clever and successful, or that rich Indian lawyers look down their noses at him; it even doesn't matter that most of the new factories seem to be owned by Japanese investors. He has begun to get active in the Partai Islam se-Malaysia (Malaysian Islamic Party) because it represents to him the true spirit of Islamic progress. In his own lifetime, God willing, Malaysia will truly belong to the Malays once again.

A Minibus Driver

Six days a week, Peter Hitam drives his minibus, a new Mitsubishi twelve-seater, back and forth between Kota Kinabalu and Kota Belud on Sabah's main highway, two round trips every day. He doesn't own the bus, but instead leases it from a businessman in the city who owns a whole fleet of them.

Asked about his unusual name, Peter explains that he is a Christian Kadazan, and prefers to use his baptismal name; he has a "village name" too, but he likes Peter better. He refuses to work on Sundays, although it would mean more money for his family. He likes to attend church with his family; he has a good singing voice and is a regular member of the church choir. The church is a simple wooden building with a small steeple, not far from his home in the outskirts of Kota

Kinabalu. It was founded many years ago by an Evangelical missionary from America, but the minister is a Kadazan now.

Peter Hitam lives with his wife and two young children in a typical *kampung* house. It is small but comfortable, a wooden building with a wood-shingle roof built on stilts about six feet above the ground. That is very convenient, he explains; being above the ground provides a cool breeze, and prevents flooding during the monsoon rains. Besides, the space beneath the house provides shade for the chickens, dogs, and goats that roam freely through the village. His parents live nearby, and half the people in the village are cousins of one sort or another. His brother has moved to an apartment in the city to be nearer to his job as a construction worker, and his sister lives in a *kampung* a few miles away; they often come home on Sundays so the whole family can spend the day together.

Being a minibus driver is a good job, and he does his job well. His open, friendly personality is good for business. When he and his assistant park at the Kota Kinabalu minibus terminal early in the morning, and again in the afternoon, they call out, "Belud, Belud," until every seat in his bus is taken. If it gets very late, he will leave with less than a full bus, but he doesn't like to because then the run will not make as much profit. Many of his passengers do not go all the way to Kota Belud, especially the market women who pile up the center aisle of the bus with their bulging bundles. He lets them off wherever they want to stop, and he and his assistant keep their eyes peeled all along the way for new passengers to pick up. He has many Bajau friends in Kota Belud, where he stops for a layover each morning and afternoon.

Driving is dangerous, he admits. Almost every day he passes an accident along the road, and he himself has been forced off the road

Minibus driver, Sabah.

many times. The log trucks and big buses are the worst; they think they own the road. But he doesn't worry about it too much. "When my time comes, God will call me home, whether it's in my bus tomorrow or in my bed when I'm an old man. God will decide."

A Flight Attendant

Fatima Hussein is young, pretty, and very talented. She has to be; there were more than twenty applicants for each available place when she got her job as a flight attendant for Malaysian Airlines. Better still, she flies international routes, making her one of the airline's elite workers. She is bilingual in Malay and English, can hold her own in a conversation in Mandarin Chinese, and knows enough Japanese to take care of her Japanese passengers.

Ms. Hussein grew up in Johor Baru. Her parents are comfortably wealthy; her father got a government loan years ago under the New Economic Policy and started a factory making latex gloves. He turned out to be a good businessman and a careful manager, and the business prospered. It was easy to expand; whenever he made enough money, he bought additional dipping and drying machines and hired more workers. The international AIDS epidemic created a huge increase in demand for sterile gloves; now his factory works two shifts a day, and he airfreights his products all over the world through Singapore.

Ms. Hussein's parents consider themselves modern and progressive, so they made sure their daughter had the best education they could afford. She went to a private girls' school that followed the English curriculum, with a heavy academic workload, plenty of field hockey and other sports, and good training in how to behave as a cultured, upper-class person. Many of her classmates were Chinese and Indian, so Ms. Hussein grew up thinking of herself as a multicultural person. Now that she's working and old enough to vote, she has thought more about Malaysia's future and feels that the country must become truly multicultural if it is to survive and progress. It is ridiculous, she says, for people to choose their friends only from among their own ethnic group. And she has only scorn for the "hooded ones," as she calls the Malay religious girls in their *hijabs.* She herself buys fashionable clothes when she is in Tokyo or Hong Kong, and she also likes how she looks in her nicely tailored *batik* flight attendant's dress.

It makes her angry to know that many Malays think that modern young women like herself are "fast." "I'm a good girl," she says indignantly. "When I'm abroad there's usually not time to do anything but rest up for the next flight. Or I go shopping with my girl friends. I don't play around." Still, she worries about what will happen when she gets a bit older and has to quit flying. The company makes sure that its flight attendants are always young and pretty, and expects them to leave to get married by the time they're thirty. She doesn't want to marry a traditional Malay man who would expect a submissive, obedient wife.

"Malaysia is a hard place to be a modern young woman," she says sadly. "I like who I am, but I wonder if there is really a place for me here."

A Longhouse Child

Salleh Endang is a young boy of the Kayan tribe of Sarawak. He and his family live with about forty other families in a longhouse built near the bank of a small stream, a tributary of the mighty Baram River. His father is a lumberjack; like most of the adult men of the longhouse, he works in the logging camps that cut timber and ship it down the river for export. Salleh is ten years old, and he is supposed to go to the elementary school that serves several longhouses in his district. But he often skips school, and the school officer complains to his parents about it. His mother scolds him about not going to school, but he is daring enough to pay no attention to her; his father does make him attend classes when he is home, but he's often away.

It is much more fun for Salleh and his friends to play in the forest, or to tag along when the grown-ups go fishing or run errands up and down the river in their motorized dugouts. Salleh already knows how to handle a boat very well. His mother spends most of her time working in her vegetable garden or tending the longhouse's pepper plantation, and Salleh is expected to help her whenever a lot of work needs to be done. Still, there is plenty of time for play. Salleh especially enjoys racing up and down along the longhouse's wide verandah with his playmates, ignoring the disapproving looks of the grannies who sit weaving *ikat* cloth on their looms all day, or making split bamboo mats by hand. The only time he knows he is in for a serious scolding is if he and his friends spill any of the pepper berries drying on mats in the sun. He has learned to be careful about running around; once his leg fell through a place where the verandah's bamboo flooring had become rotten, and he still has a long scar on his thigh to show for it.

Salleh loves to listen to the stories that the old men tell about head-hunting in the old days, and about fierce chiefs with names like Bald Hawk and Blood Flow. The old men, and old women too, also tell wonderful stories about the gods, like the one about the girl who was turned to stone because she made fun of the Fish People in the river. The old men look very impressive, with big blue tattoos on their arms and shoulders. Sometimes Salleh's grandfather will go into the forest and shoot a couple of wood pigeons for dinner with his blowgun; it's easier to use an air rifle, but he likes to show that he still can do it in the old way.

An Iban longhouse, Sarawak. Anywhere from thirty to one hundred families might share a longhouse, which has private family rooms along one side, an open common space on the other, and a wide verandah for cooking, recreation, and drying the village's crop of black pepper on large woven mats.

Once in a while a tour guide from Miri will bring a few foreign tourists to the longhouse to stay overnight. Salleh enjoys that very much, although the first time he saw tourists he thought they looked strange and frightening. Now he's glad when they come, because the longhouse puts on a big feast that everyone enjoys. There is singing and dancing, and the old people enact some of the tribe's old rituals, such as sacrificing a white rooster and sprinkling its blood on the floor. But Salleh notices that the old men avoid singing the really sacred songs that are only used at the Hornbill Festival and other ceremonies for the tribe itself. When the tourists depart, they always give presents to the longhouse, such as cartons of cigarettes, candy, T-shirts, or spools of fishing line. The longhouse headman makes sure that every family gets a fair share.

The Malay teacher at the schoolhouse tells Salleh and his friends that they must think about the future. But to Salleh, the future seems very far away, especially when you live in a longhouse in the midst of a beautiful forest, in a warm and loving community that knows children need to enjoy their childhood. As the grown-ups know, the future will come soon enough.

A College Student

Lam Boon Sah is a freshman at the University of Malaya in Kuala Lumpur. His father is a bank branch manager in Port Dickson, and the family also earns a modest income from a small tin dredge that they own in Perak. The family lives in a comfortable, modern house, where Boon Sah's mother takes care of his younger brother and sister. At home the Lams try to speak only English together, because they think that is modern and progressive. With her friends Mrs. Lam almost always speaks Cantonese; Malay is for her maid, for taxi drivers, and for shopkeepers when she has to go to a non-Chinese-owned store. Their world is comfortably Chinese and middle class, but at the university, their son has to contend with an environment where advantages go to the *bumiputra*s.

Boon Sah shares a cramped apartment in Kuala Lumpur with two roommates; he spends as little time as possible there because it is so dingy and drab, and full of cockroaches. He takes a bus every day to the university. When he's not going to classes, he hangs out with his Chinese friends.

Boon Sah worked hard in high school so that he could pass the university entrance exams, but now he is not a very good student. "What's the point?" he asks. "My path is blocked at every turn. The *bumi*s get everything; there will be nothing left for me." What he really wants is to transfer to a college in the United States, but that would be possible only if he got very high grades in his first year at the university. But he is so discouraged about his future that he doesn't like to study, and his grades are not very good. Life seems to Boon Sah to be an endless circle of disappointment.

As a way of avoiding thinking about his problems, and also of avoiding studying, Boon Sah likes to go with his friends to their favorite coffee house near the university campus. They spend hours nursing small cups of coffee and plates of Western-style pastries so that they can stay as long as possible; they like the coffee shop much better than their student apartments, or even the university library. They talk about clothes and music and girls, and especially about the big business deals they hope to make after they graduate. They avoid talking about politics, though; you never know who might be listening, and saying anything critical of the government can lead to big trouble.

Even more fun than the coffee house is hanging around the big shopping mall in the same neighborhood. Boon Sah and his friends put on their newest clothes—they think of themselves as "sharp dressers"—and walk from shop to shop, looking at more new clothes in the windows, or listening to the latest compact discs. Sometimes they stand around in a group in front of the music store, making remarks to passing girls. Usually the girls ignore them and walk on angrily, but sometimes they giggle with embarrassment, and then Boon Sah feels good that he and his friends were noticed. Alone, Boon Sah is very shy around girls, and he's never actually had a date with one yet, but he thinks about them all the time.

Music is important to Boon Sah and his friends. They know all the

Lat (Mohamad Nor Khalid) is Malaysia's most famous cartoonist, known for his perceptive commentary on Malaysian daily life. In this cartoon his hero, Mat Som, a boy from a rural kampung living in the big city, walks with his jeans-clad girlfriend, as urban "mod boys" in bizarre clothing look on in amazement. "In this age, which young man marries his father's choice?" By permission of Kampung Boy Sdn. Bhd.

rock groups from America and England, but they prefer the groups from Hong Kong because they sing in Chinese. Once they went to a concert by the Johor Baru heavy-metal group Search, and although they felt somewhat out of place in the mostly Malay audience, they agreed that the music itself was pretty good.

For Lam Boon Sah, four years at the university are a time of transition between childhood and the adult world. He doesn't think very much about the future, because it seems mostly out of his hands anyway. He almost certainly will never realize his dream of studying abroad. After he graduates, his father will help him to find a business job in Port Dickson, and a few years later he will marry a Chinese girl picked out for him by his parents. If he somehow manages to find in himself a level of ambition and determination that has shown no sign of being there so far, perhaps he and his wife will emigrate to Canada or Australia, where they won't have to think about *bumi*s anymore.

Most likely, Lam Boon Sah will remain in Malaysia, a solid, hard-working middle-class Chinese. He will mind his own business, take life as it comes, and try to find a way to have a good life in a nation that will never feel quite his own.

Malaysia and Brunei in the World Today

Since gaining independence, both Malaysia and Brunei have achieved remarkable success in social, political, and economic development. The challenges facing the two nations in the 1990's and beyond are mostly what might be called the challenges of success. Economic growth and prosperity create pressure on both countries to play a larger role in the world, not only in trade and other economic activity, but also in politics, diplomacy, tourism, defense, and other international fields. Policies that were appropriate when Malaysia and Brunei could think of themselves as small, underdeveloped, and mainly preoccupied with internal affairs will be less appropriate as they emerge increasingly into a broader international arena.

Malaysia

Malaysia has one of the world's fastest-growing economies, yet the speed of its economic expansion has brought growing pains. In many ways Malaysia's social, political, and even economic structures have not yet caught up to the rapid pace of the country's economic development. Religious and ethnic issues, as well as problems of political stability and regionalism, will shape the country's responses to its new-found prosperity.

Religious and Ethnic Issues

The New Economic Policy (NEP) instituted in 1970 was designed to improve the lot of *bumiputra*s in relation to that of Malaysian Chinese and Indians. Initially the NEP was intended to stay in force for twenty years, expiring in 1990; in that year it was reenacted, with modifications, for another twenty-year period. In its first two decades, the NEP had mixed success; it undoubtedly did advance the overall economic interests of the *bumiputra*s, but more unevenly and to a lesser degree than its proponents had hoped. Prime Minister Mahathir bin Mohamad sought to justify a policy that many observers felt had succeeded only in producing a few Malay millionaires: "If these few Malays are not enriched the poor Malays will not gain either. It is the Chinese who will continue to live in huge houses and regard the Malays as only fit to drive their cars." On the other hand, hopes that an improved economic status for Malays would lead to a more integrated Malaysia have generally been disappointed; socially, politically, and religiously, Malaysia remains a nation of separate communities.

The NEP's "affirmative action" provisions for *bumiputra*s led to some resentment on the part of Malaysia's Chinese and Indians, who

A young boy in a fishing village on the east coast of the Malay Peninsula.

felt that they were unfairly being held back. As one Chinese student said recently, with a shrug of resignation, "It is very difficult for a non-Malay to get into the civil service—and equally difficult to rise." These complaints, however, were rather mild during the high-growth years of the 1980's. Most Chinese and Indians did not mind having a smaller slice of Malaysia's economic pie, as long as the whole pie was getting larger very quickly. Any future slowdown in economic growth will rapidly translate into Chinese and Indian complaints of discrimination and deprivation. Already tens of thousands of Malaysian Chinese, feeling their road to advancement blocked at home, have emigrated abroad. And Malaysian Indian political leaders point out that the New Economic Policies discriminate in favor of Malays despite the fact that rural Indians are among the country's poorest citizens. Meanwhile, many Malays are frustrated by the reality that after twenty years of affirmative action, the Malaysian economy is still dominated by non-Malays.

Meanwhile, religion has increasingly divided Malaysians from each other. Islamic consciousness has grown steadily within Malaysia's Malay community, visible in everything from religious dress to a renewal of interest in Arabic script, from rapidly growing Islamic universities to political activism by Muslim fundamentalists. As an expression of personal religious values, this movement is admirable, but many non-Malay Malaysians fear that the Islamic revival is also an expression of Malay ethnic solidarity. They fear that the Malays are showing not only renewed faith in their religion, but also a stronger drive to use Islam to dominate other Malaysians.

Chinese, Indians, and other groups (such as the Christian Kadazans of Sabah) have also become worried by the extent to which the Malay Islamic revival has been reflected in new laws. For example, Arabic script is now taught by law in public primary schools, even in those that have mixed or predominantly non-Malay student bodies. More con-

The historic Friday Mosque in downtown Kuala Lumpur is dwarfed by the modern office towers that surround it—a symbol of Malaysia's difficult ambition to emphasize both Islamic orthodoxy and economic modernization.

troversially, the state of Selangor passed laws in 1989 that allowed minors to convert to Islam without the consent of their parents, and that provided that minor children of parents who converted to Islam would automatically be considered Muslims. Many Chinese, especially, feared that the vigorous efforts of the *dakwah* movement to gain new converts to Islam would be aimed at their children, with government support.

These issues, the complexities of which dominate Malaysian public affairs, suggest that the most important challenge facing Malaysia in the

Baba-Nyonya-style Chinese houses, Melaka. These large and often ornate houses were built by wealthy merchants at the end of the nineteenth century. They have shops or offices on the ground floor, and residential quarters above.

future is that of finding a way to maintain a stable balance among the country's diverse ethnic and religious groups. Officially, the Malaysian government portrays the country as one happy, multiethnic family. Unofficially, too, in dozens of small ways, it is clear that people in positions of power often try to avoid offending ethnic sensibilities. For example, in television and magazine advertisements, models are usually chosen (except in cases where products are clearly designed to appeal to one ethnic group or another) for a kind of generic Southeast Asian beauty that is not recognizably Malay, Chinese, or Indian.

Political and Regional Issues

In the political arena too, ethnic issues often dominate all others. While Malaysia's political parties have been remarkably fluid, fracturing and converging in ever-changing patterns, politics in Malaysia is ethnic politics. Political parties, by whatever name and with whatever leadership, are essentially Malay, Chinese, and Indian parties; or, in East Malaysia, are based on other ethnic identities. In Sarawak, for example, a Malay-Melanau alliance is challenged by an Iban party.

Malaysia is a federation, which means that the thirteen separate states retain significant powers not granted to the national government. Although federal law overrules state law whenever the two conflict, many areas of control lie primarily with the states, and so policies may differ considerably from one part of the country to another. For example, all decisions governing land use are under the control of the states, which makes it difficult to formulate national policy on such issues as industrial development or forest conservation. More seriously, party politics operates at least as vigorously on the state level as on the national level. The Malaysian prime minister must devote a large, and perhaps excessive, amount of time and energy to building and maintaining political alliances at the state level in order to hold on to national political power. For example, in 1983 Prime Minister Mahathir tried to win a constitutional change that would restrict the power of Malaysia's king. The issue was finally settled by a compromise, but in the process the prime minister so angered the rulers of West Malaysia's nine remaining sultanates that he had to spend years cultivating allies among the sultans to try to repair the damage.

The most dramatic example of regionalism in Malaysia is the division between the Peninsula and the northern Borneo states. Sarawak and Sabah joined the Malaysian Federation voluntarily in 1963 and have remained loyal to the ideal of national unity; no one thinks that there is any serious prospect of either of those states seceding from the federation. Nevertheless, in both states there is a steady current of popular feeling that Kuala Lumpur tries to dominate East Malaysia too much politically. One of Malaysia's more serious political crises occurred in 1987, when the Mahathir government tried (unsuccessfully) to prevent the seating of a newly elected government in Sabah that was dominated by a Kadazan Christian party. And on the other hand, many people in Sarawak and Sabah resent what they feel is the national government's neglect of their economic needs.

The most basic political challenge facing Malaysia in the future, however, is political reform. By the standards of the many Third World nations that have gained their independence since World War II, Malaysia is a democracy, and a stable and successful one. Yet Malaysia is also far from being a democracy by the standards that prevail in North America or Western Europe. UMNO, the ruling party, has in effect undermined representative government by ensuring that electoral districts are heavily weighted in favor of rural areas; this means that the Chinese-dominated cities are under-represented in national politics. Moreover, UMNO engages in practices that would be considered scandalous and illegal in a country like the United States. For example, UMNO has been a major beneficiary of the New Economic Policies, and owns—as a political party—a large network of banks, trading corporations, industrial concerns, and other enterprises. To get some idea of what that means, imagine what people in America would think if the United States government lent money to the Republican Party to buy a majority share of the stock in General Motors.

The ruling party has taken other steps as well to ensure that it stays in power. Marxist and other leftist political parties are banned, and some outspoken critics of the government have been jailed under the provisions of the Internal Security Act, which allows the government to place people suspected of political crimes under "preventive detention." And because the government controls radio and television, and censorship is regularly imposed on the press, opposition parties have little chance to present their positions to the public.

In large part because of these conditions, relatively few Malaysians participate actively in politics. Real political power in the country still rests in the hands of a small number of people, such as political party professionals, members of traditional elite groups, and the very wealthy. Many ordinary individuals participate in the political process only by voting, and voting is often an expression of membership in a political party, ethnic group, trade association, or other organization rather than of individual choice. (Of course, it can be argued that people advance their own political interests most effectively by voting for the interests of their group.) Human rights and civil liberties are guaranteed by the constitution in principle, but weakly guarded by the government in practice. Antidemocratic practices naturally discourage people from expressing their views freely or participating actively in politics.

A second great challenge for Malaysia in the 1990's and beyond, therefore, lies in strengthening the democratic process. With greater democracy will come a stronger and more truly representative national government—a government better equipped to deal with issues of religion and ethnicity, regionalism, and economic development. On the other hand, some Malaysians argue that because of the country's volatile ethnic politics, a broadening of democratic institutions would be dangerous and destabilizing.

The Economy

Malaysia's rapid economic growth has rested on a triple foundation of private enterprise, state corporations, and foreign investment. Private entrepreneurship has been most evident and successful among Malaysia's traditional economic elites, the Chinese and Indian communities. State corporations, such as the PERNAS state trading company, have operated under the New Economic Policy to provide new opportunities for ethnic Malays and other *bumiputras*, and have engaged in a wide range of ventures from investment in heavy industry to the formation of agricultural marketing cooperatives. Foreign investment has come most notably from Japan but also from elsewhere in Asia (Taiwan, South Korea, Hong Kong, Singapore) and beyond (the United States and Western Europe, often through subsidiary companies based in Singapore). The establishment of manufacturing facilities in Malaysia under foreign ownership has contributed especially to Malaysia's exports of manufactured goods; Malaysia is now the world's leading exporter of semiconductors, the world's second leading exporter of air conditioners, and one of the world's largest exporters of latex goods such as surgical gloves.

Malaysia's economic boom has produced a number of strains, however. Banks, the stock market, and similar institutions are not strong enough to meet the demands of rapid growth. Corruption and misman-

The Economy of Malaysia

INDUSTRY (1988):

ELECTRICAL PRODUCTS: US$2.16 billion

FOOD: US$2.11 billion

PETROLEUM REFINING: US$885.5 million

TRANSPORTATION EQUIPMENT: US$439.4 million

TEXTILES: US$172.8 million

OTHER MANUFACTURED GOODS: US$2.50 billion

AGRICULTURE AND FORESTRY (1988):

RUBBER: 1.826 million tons (1.66 million metric tons)

PALM OIL: 6.215 million tons (5.65 million metric tons)

LUMBER: 1.62 billion board feet (3.65 million cubic meters)

RICE: 1.914 million tons (1.74 million metric tons)

PEPPER: 21,329 tons (19,390 metric tons)

PINEAPPLES: 157,300 tons (143,000 metric tons)

OIL AND NATURAL GAS (1988):

CRUDE PETROLEUM: 197.8 million barrels

LIQUEFIED NATURAL GAS: 6.82 million tons (6.2 million metric tons)

MINING (1988):

TIN: 31.79 million tons (28.9 million metric tons)

EXPORTS (1988):

MANUFACTURED GOODS: US$3.10 billion

PETROLEUM/PETROLEUM PRODUCTS: US$2.28 billion

LUMBER: US$1.49 billion

RUBBER: US$1.95 billion

PALM OIL: US$1.68 billion

TIN: US$338.7 million

TOURIST ARRIVALS (1989):   3.9 million

REVENUE FROM TOURISM (1989):   US$842.3 million

IMPORTS (1988):

MACHINERY AND TRANSPORT EQUIPMENT: US$7.20 billion

MANUFACTURED GOODS: US$3.65 billion

FOOD: US$1.43 billion

agement produced a series of spectacular financial scandals and bank failures in the 1980's that impeded economic growth and damaged investor confidence. A government policy of "privatizing" a number of public corporations in the late 1980's led to a storm of allegations that Finance Minister Daim Zainuddin was enriching himself through corruption, kickbacks, nepotism, and conflict of interest, though no legal action was ever taken against him. The rise to new importance of manufacturing and petroleum/natural gas has masked, to some extent, difficulties in tin and in plantation crops, Malaysia's more traditional economic strongholds. Many small, uneconomical tin mines have had to shut down following a decline in the world price for tin. Similarly, many family-run rubber and palm-oil plantations are too small to succeed, rural poverty among smallholders is a persistent problem, and many smallholders have left the countryside to seek factory work in the cities.

Foreign investment has led to a curious imbalance in Malaysia's employment picture. Foreign-owned factories have been attracted by Malaysia's relatively low wages, and industrial workers are in demand; on the other hand, foreign ownership and management means that not enough management-level jobs are available to provide employment for all of Malaysia's highly educated urban population. Malaysia is rising from a "Third World" status to that of a "Newly Industrialized Nation." In order to continue this progress, the country will have to move away from being a source of cheap labor for foreign-owned factories and toward having a more broadly based national economy dominated by domestic investment and management.

In the longer term, Malaysia faces a labor problem of a different sort: not enough workers. Malaysia's present population of just over 17 million simply does not provide enough workers to satisfy the country's potential for foreign investment. In other words, if the country had more

The Fate of the Rain Forest

About 80 percent of the area of Malaysia is classified as forest land, but that figure has become misleading in recent years because of rapid deforestation. By some estimates, at present rates of cutting the Malay Peninsula will have no old-growth forest left by 1997 (except for areas protected in national parks and other reserves), while the virgin forest of Sabah will last for only a few years longer. In Sarawak, which is both larger and proportionately more heavily forested than the Peninsula or Sabah, the forest will endure into the twenty-first century; nevertheless, one third of Sarawak's trees were cut down between 1983 and 1990. Like the Amazon Basin, Zaire, and other major rain-forest regions of the world, Malaysia risks being turned, in the space of a few decades, from a rich storehouse of natural biological diversity to a land of tree plantations and barren scrub.

Timber exports, principally to Japan, account for slightly more than one tenth of Malaysia's gross export earnings; forestry is a major source of employment. A rapid decline in earnings and employment from logging would clearly hurt the country's economy. Nevertheless, conservation organizations both within Malaysia and throughout the world have called upon the Malaysian government to slow the destruction of the forest and to adopt better, more conservation-minded forestry methods.

The response of the Malaysian government has been to resist external pressure; it takes the position that the industrial countries of the world (including Japan, the United States, and the nations of Western Europe), having already gotten rich, have no right to hold back the economic development of Third World countries. On the other hand, this rather self-righteous position is to some extent a

mask for the huge financial stake that a few government officials and rich owners of timber concessions have in continuing to cut down the forest. At the grass-roots level, domestic opposition to logging is growing. While many Iban in Sarawak work as lumberjacks, others have staged sit-down strikes in the forest to prevent the construction of new logging roads. Organizations of native peoples in Sarawak and Sabah have joined forces with similar groups in Brazil, Zaire, and elsewhere to publicize the struggle to save the forest.

One partial conservation measure likely to be adopted soon in Malaysia is legislation banning the export of raw logs. This is designed as much to aid the Malaysian plywood and furniture industries as it is to slow the cutting of the forests, but it would have that effect as well. Brunei has already enacted a total ban on the cutting of old-growth forest. But with petroleum revenues due to decline steadily in the next two decades, Bruneians may be tempted to resume logging as a new source of national income.

The rapidly growing worldwide environmental movement, coupled with worries about the "greenhouse effect," ensures that international pressure on Malaysia to slow the rate of deforestation will become increasingly strong in the 1990's. Growing numbers of Malaysians, too, may realize that the benefits of the rain forest for everything from climate stabilization to finding new drugs from forest plants to providing a lure for foreign tourists may outweigh the short-term benefits from logging. But by the time attitudes and laws change to bring about effective conservation of Malaysia's rain forests, there may not be very much left to save.

Only a small patch of forest remains after a logging operation in Sarawak. About 15,000 square miles of forest—one third of Sarawak's total forest area—was clear-cut between 1983 and 1990. Courtesy of Atsuko Otsuka people, it would attract more foreign investment, and the economy would grow even faster. In contrast to much of the world, where family planning and population limitation have high priority, the Malaysian government is energetically promoting faster population growth. The current goals are a population of 20 million in the year 2000, and 23 million by 2010. The government expects that most of the population growth will take place in the *bumiputra* community. (Some of this growth will come because of immigration from Indonesia and the Philippines, which is illegal but tolerated by the government.) Although the Chinese and Indians will also increase in numbers, their percentage share of the total population will shrink. Of course, if government plans for population growth succeed, the country will also face even more poverty and environmental destruction.

Related to increased population growth is a plan to spread new industrial development more evenly throughout the country, in part to compensate for a future decline in importance of mining, plantation crops, and forestry. At the moment, Malaysia's economic modernization and growth has been very uneven, region by region. Growth has been most conspicuous in a few areas such as Kuala Lumpur and the surrounding Klang River Valley; the state of Johor and particularly the city of Johor Baru, strategically located near the international port of Singapore; the east coast state of Terengganu, spurred by petroleum and natural gas development; and the area around Kota Kinabalu in Sabah, which has become a "boomtown" because of growth in logging, construction, and manufacturing. Though development naturally tends to follow resources, this has had the effect of sharpening the contrasts between rich and poor regions of the country. In both relatively rich and relatively poor regions, future economic growth will depend in part on improvements in transportation, communications, and other basic public facilities. Even now, Malaysia's roads and railroads are overburdened everywhere; new roads and rails are urgently needed.

Malaysia's economic growth has also been helped in part by a dramatic increase in tourism. Take a "Malaysia Stopover," the Malaysian Airlines brochure says. Enjoy "the sparkling white sands on long lazy beaches. The lush tropical rainforests. The colourful tapestry of festivals, cuisines, and lifestyles in a multi-racial society." And tourists have responded; in 1989 nearly four million foreigners visited Malaysia, adding $850 million to the national economy. Malaysian tourist-industry officials forecast that the number of arrivals will increase to ten million by the year 2000. For this to happen smoothly also will require a steady increase in investment in transportation, hotels, resorts, and other facilities. The growth of the tourist industry also raises questions—as nearly every issue in Malaysia seems to do—of religion and ethnicity. Tourists will not come if Malaysia gets a reputation for ethnic strife; they may not come if Malaysia's national image becomes one of Islamic conservatism. Conversely, what will be the impact on Malaysia's modest, conservative Muslim majority of the arrival of millions of sun-and-fun-loving tourists demanding more beach resorts and night-clubs?

Malaysia clearly faces a promising economic future, but managing economic growth wisely in the context of Malaysia's exceptionally complex and diverse society will be a challenge for the country's leadership for decades to come.

International Relations

Since gaining independence, Malaysia has consistently pursued a foreign policy of neutrality and international cooperation. Malaysia's foremost priority is the peace and security of Southeast Asia, and to that end it has taken a leading role in the Association of Southeast Asian

Nations (ASEAN). Within the ASEAN framework, Malaysia helped to coordinate a regional response in the late 1970's and early 1980's to the Vietnamese invasion of Cambodia, and since then has been active diplomatically in pursuing a political solution to the Cambodian question.

Malaysia has resisted suggestions from other ASEAN nations that the association should coordinate its regional defense policies. Malaysia contends that it is important that ASEAN remain a political and economic alliance but not compromise its neutrality by seeming to become a defensive alliance. The Malaysian government has been a strong supporter of an ASEAN plan to make Southeast Asia a "Zone of Peace, Freedom, and Neutrality" (ZOPFAN). In other ASEAN matters, Malaysia supported the inclusion of Papua New Guinea as an "observer member" of the association, a step that may lead in the future to full membership. This accords with a broader Malaysian policy of upgrading its relations with other South Pacific nations such as Vanuatu and Fiji, partly in the hope of expanding Malaysian deep-sea fishing in the western Pacific.

Malaysia has also worked within an ASEAN framework to deal with its most painful international problem, the arrival on Malaysia's shores of tens of thousands of Vietnamese "boat people," many of whom are ethnic Chinese. Until the late 1980's, Malaysia voluntarily ran an extensive, and expensive, network of refugee camps for the boat people. It refused to accept them as permanent refugees, but it allowed them to stay until they could be resettled elsewhere. In recent years, however, Malaysia has said that it is overwhelmed by the problem, and now its patrol boats tow refugee ships back into international waters before they can land. The other ASEAN nations have joined Malaysia in calling for a comprehensive international plan for dealing with the problem.

Relations between Malaysia and the other ASEAN nations have

generally been good, but problems have arisen from time to time. The Philippines has never renounced its old claim to sovereignty over Sabah, and although that problem is now dormant, it has not disappeared. The government of the Philippines, in turn, has sometimes expressed suspicions that Malaysia is sympathetic to the Moro separatist guerrillas who are fighting to create a new Muslim state of their own in the southern Philippines. Sabah is also the focus of discord between Malaysia and Indonesia. Malaysia wants Indonesia to curb the flow of illegal immigrants to Sabah; Indonesia says that it is trying, but can do little to solve the problem.

Relations between Malaysia and Singapore were somewhat distant and wary from the time Singapore left the Federation of Malaysia in 1963 to the early 1980's, but they have since improved, and now are excellent. Economic development in the southern Peninsula, particularly the state of Johor, is closely tied to Malaysian access to Singapore's international business community and its superb port facilities. Relations are likely to grow closer still with the planned construction of a second bridge linking Malaysia to Singapore. Nevertheless, Malaysia protested vehemently in 1989 when Singapore offered naval and air-base facilities to the United States in the event that U.S. bases in the Philippines were closed. This caused a brief chill in Malaysia-Singapore relations.

Malaysia's most persistent problem within ASEAN concerns the Malaysian-Thai border. Small bands of communist guerrillas, remnants of the "Emergency" of the 1950's, have operated on both sides of the border, seeking to overthrow both the Malaysian and Thai governments. Malaysian-Thai military cooperation along the border has been limited, however, in part because an unrelated rebellion of ethnic Malay separatists in southern Thailand has aroused Thai suspicions of the loyalties of Malaysia's armed forces. There are hopeful signs that these problems may soon be resolved. On December 2, 1989, the Malay Communist Party signed an agreement with the governments of Malaysia and Thailand in which the guerrillas pledged to lay down their arms and declared their loyalty to the Malaysian government. This ended, at least on paper, forty-one years of communist insurrection on the Malaysian-Thai border.

Elsewhere in Asia, Malaysia has friendly but restrained relations with the "little dragons," South Korea, Taiwan, and Hong Kong, its principal competitors among Asia's Newly Industrialized Countries. Relations with China have been cool ever since China supported the communist insurgency in Malaya in the 1950's, and they took a turn for the worse after China's suppression of its Tiananmen Square democracy movement in 1989. Malaysians need special permission from the government to travel to China, and that permission is often denied, especially in the case of ethnic Chinese citizens. A "Look East" policy in the 1980's succeeded in attracting a great deal of Japanese investment in Malaysia, and the Malaysian government openly admires Japan as an example of efficient economic development. On the other hand, many Malaysians view Japanese investment, with its many strings attached, as a form of economic exploitation. They also complain about Japan's unwillingness to buy Malaysian manufactured goods (in contrast to timber, rubber, and other raw materials).

As an active member of the Islamic Conference, Malaysia has played a leading role in efforts of the Conference to promote the interests of the Palestinians in the Middle East. Malaysia has also taken a vocal pro-Palestinian stance in the United Nations.

Malaysia is a member of the British Commonwealth, but has not been active in its affairs except to urge that the Commonwealth promote a "north-south" dialogue between the world's developed and developing nations. Malaysia's disregard for the Commonwealth reflects its perception that British power had waned to insignificance in Asia, and that Malaysia's main interests lay with ASEAN. But Malaysia's ruling elite has been generally pro-British, and wealthy young Malaysians typically attend British universities. Malaysians were outraged, therefore, when the British government drastically increased tuition fees for Commonwealth students in 1981. In response, the Malaysian government actively discouraged the importation of British goods; the slogan was "Buy British Last." Relations gradually improved again during the late 1980's, however, in part on the basis of a good relationship between Prime Minister Mahathir and Britain's former Prime Minister Thatcher. Among other Commonwealth nations, Australia has important trade and investment ties with Malaysia, but relations between the two countries have often been strained by open criticism in the Australian press of human-rights abuses in Malaysia.

Relations between Malaysia and the United States are good. Malaysia actively promotes American investment in the national economy, in part as a counterweight to Japanese investment. Trade between the two countries has grown significantly, though Malaysia objects to what it regards as American unfair trade practices in the form of tariffs and quotas on some inexpensive manufactured goods, notably textiles and clothing. The United States replaced Great Britain as the country of choice for young Malaysians seeking a university education abroad in the 1980's; by the end of that decade, an estimated 50,000 Malaysians were attending colleges in America, many of them on government scholarships. In broader foreign-policy terms, Malaysia has applauded America's commitment to a strong military presence in the western Pacific, which it sees as a deterrent to Soviet "meddling" in Indochina. That policy motive has faded as Soviet domestic difficulties have curbed the U.S.S.R.'s international activities, but although determinedly neutral, Malaysia continues to approve of America's role as a peacekeeper in Asia. Malaysia has also become a significant customer for American arms, as it seeks to upgrade its own capacity to defend the seas and skies between West and East Malaysia.

Relations between Malaysia and the countries of Western Europe are friendly, but limited mainly to trade and investment. Relations with the U.S.S.R. have been cool and almost nonexistent.

It seems clear that the future of Malaysian foreign relations will follow the course already firmly established: Malaysia will pursue a policy of neutrality; active participation in the United Nations and the Islamic Conference, and, through those organizations, symbolic solidarity with the developing countries of the world; expanded trade and investment ties with noncommunist industrialized nations; and, most importantly of all, regional cooperation within the framework of ASEAN.

Brunei

Since achieving independence at the beginning of 1984, Brunei has nominally been a constitutional monarchy; but whereas that term usually describes a government in which the monarch acts as a head of state while politics is practiced by elected officials, Brunei's constitution ensures that all political power remains in the hands of the sultan and his family. Rather than resembling constitutional monarchies like Great Britain and Japan, Brunei's government is closer to those of traditional Islamic sultanates like Qatar or Bahrain.

In effect, the sultan of Brunei and his family have offered the people of Brunei a political bargain: Bruneians get stability, security, and prosperity from their government, in exchange for giving up any claim to democratic politics and guaranteed human rights. This bargain has apparently been acceptable to most of the people of Brunei, who have shown little interest in changing it; the small number of people who have agitated for political democracy and human rights have been rigorously suppressed through imprisonment or exile. The problem with this approach to domestic politics is that it seems to limit severely Brunei's ability to play the larger regional and international role that the nation's wealth might suggest. As the events of 1989–90 in Central Europe demonstrated, democracy is highly contagious; any nation that wishes to avoid democratization must place itself in quarantine.

The effects of this self-imposed isolation are readily apparent to every visitor to Brunei. The national airport is new, large, and beautifully equipped, but it handles far fewer flights than it is capable of. In keeping with Brunei's role as a major exporter of petroleum and natural gas, and its role as a regional center of financial services, business visitors are welcome, but tourism is not encouraged and tourists find few facilities designed for their convenience. The capital city, Bandar Seri Begawan, boasts a large and attractive international conference center, but it stands empty much of the time. Most dramatically, although Brunei is surrounded by the Malaysian state of Sarawak, hardly any roads join the two territories, and overland public transportation between Brunei and Sarawak is nonexistent.

Brunei is by far the most diplomatically timid of the ASEAN nations. Although it has played an active role in ASEAN affairs, for example by hosting the annual conference of ASEAN prime ministers in 1989, it has shied away from taking any role in regional leadership, and has usually been content to support quietly the consensus of the regional alliance's larger nations. Brunei's diplomacy within Southeast Asia tends to be personal rather than national; Brunei's good relations with its immediate neighbors seem to depend heavily on Sultan Haji Hassanal Bolkiah's close personal relationships with President Suharto of Indonesia, Prime Minister Lee Kwan Yew of Singapore, and Prime Minister Mahathir bin Mohamad of Malaysia.

In the world beyond Southeast Asia, Brunei, as a deeply committed

A Muezzin calls the faithful to prayer from the Sultan Omar Ali Saifuddin Mosque in

Islamic state, has maintained good relations throughout the Islamic world and particularly with the conservative Islamic monarchies of the Middle East. Brunei tends to support Arab League positions on Israel in the United Nations, but at the same time has opposed (often through quiet financial diplomacy) radical Islamic fundamentalism, terrorism, and Arab socialism. Brunei's relations with the non-Islamic world are

Bandur Seri Begawan.   Photo Researchers

most evident in the areas of trade in petroleum, natural gas, and refined
petroleum products, and in the sultan's personal international investments. His purchases of luxury hotels and other prime commercial
properties throughout the world have sometimes attracted considerable,
and unwelcome, publicity.

Brunei's policy of isolation may also be seen in the tiny nation's

The Economy of Brunei

PETROLEUM AND NATURAL GAS:

   OIL PRODUCTION (1988):   150,000 barrels per day

   NATURAL GAS PRODUCTION (1988):   867 million cubic feet (24.55 million cubic meters) per day

   LIQUEFIED NATURAL GAS (1986):   6.49 million tons (5.9 million metric tons)

AGRICULTURE (1988):

   RICE: 793.1 tons (721 metric tons)

   FRUIT AND VEGETABLES: 11,933 tons (10,849 metric tons)

EXPORTS (1986):

   PETROLEUM/NATURAL GAS   US$1.999 billion

   MACHINERY AND TRANSPORT: US$27.64 million

IMPORTS (1986):

   MACHINERY AND TRANSPORT EQUIPMENT: US$284 million

   MANUFACTURED GOODS: US$158 million

   FOOD AND LIVESTOCK: US$108 million

determination to maintain an independent defense force. Brunei's armed forces, though small, are well equipped with modern naval patrol vessels, helicopters, and jet aircraft—all armed with state-of-the-art missiles and other weaponry. Brunei's annual expenditures on defense have increased steadily in recent years.

Looking to the future, Brunei faces two long-term questions of economic and political change. Economically, the nation must prepare for a time when it can no longer depend on revenue from oil and gas production. Oil and gas today account for 60 percent of the nation's economic activity, and 95 percent of its exports, but underground supplies of both oil and gas are likely to be exhausted within the next twenty years. By that time, international investment of the nation's great wealth will probably provide enough income to support basic governmental expenditures of all kinds. But if Brunei is to avoid the fate of becoming a stagnant nation of pension collectors, new forms of economic activity will have to be found to replace oil and gas. Plans have already been announced to move into new areas such as pharmaceuticals, cement production, metal refining, industrial ceramics, high technology, and, most controversially, forest products. But moving from a single, tightly controlled national economic base to a more diversified economy will inevitably lead to wider and more varied international contacts, which will threaten Brunei's present political structure.

A future that includes broader participation in world business—with more international businesspeople coming to Brunei, and more Bruneians going to more places abroad—will inevitably lead to an influx of new political ideas. So, too, will a future that sees ever more Bruneian students traveling abroad for higher education and returning home to apply their new technical skills—and wanting to apply their new political consciousness as well. Tourists, too, will inevitably bring with them new attitudes, tastes, and ideas that will have an effect on the local population.

Brunei is justifiably proud of its status as a small, stable, secure, prosperous Islamic nation; whether stability, prosperity, and Islamic values can be maintained in the face of what may become overwhelming pressure for increased democratization, protection of civil and human rights, and increased diversity of choice in personal values is the greatest challenge facing Brunei in the world today.

Portraits of Brunei's Sultan Haji Hassanal Bolkiah and Crown Prince Muda Al-Muhtadee Billah adorn a public building in Bandar Seri Begawan.

Bibliography

Chapter 1

Ian Buruma, *God's Dust* (New York: Farrar, Straus & Giroux, 1989), p. 108–38, gives a concise and very insightful picture of contemporary Malaysia.

Judith Nagata, *Malaysian Mosaic: Perspectives from a Poly-Ethnic Society* (Vancouver: University of British Columbia Press, 1979), provides an excellent account of Malaysia's diverse ethnic groups from an anthropological perspective.

For a concise and well-illustrated account of the *kris* as both weapon and symbol, see Edward Frey, *The Kris: Mystic Weapon of the Malay World* (Singapore: Oxford University Press, 1986).

Several of the novels of Joseph Conrad are set in the Malay world, and capture particularly well the meeting of Asians and Westerners on the fringes of civilization. Among the best in this category are *Lord Jim*, *An Outcast of the Islands*, and *The Rescue.*

The Encyclopedia of Asian History, 4 vols. (New York: Charles Scribner's Sons, 1987), prepared under the auspices of The Asia Society, is a convenient source for information on all aspects of the history of Malaysia and Brunei; it includes excellent capsule biographies of key historical figures.

Chapters 2 and 3

The best overall treatment of the geography of Malaysia is found in J. E. Spencer and William L. Thomas, *Asia East by South: A Cultural Geography*, 2nd ed. (New York: John Wiley & Sons, 1971), although the book is now out of date on some specific details, such as the petroleum industry.

Wendy Moore, *Malaysia: Land Where the Winds Meet* (Lincolnwood, IL: Passport Books, 1989), while basically a guidebook, contains a great deal of well-presented material on Malaysian history, geography, and culture.

Alfred Russel Wallace, *The Malay Archipelago* (London: Macmillan, 1869), while concerned primarily with the East Indies, is a fascinating introduction to the geography and natural history of the Malay world in general.

Wild Malaysia (Cambridge: MIT Press, 1990) introduces Malaysia's amazing biological diversity and contemporary environmental problems through Junaidi Payne's well-informed text and 400 magnificent color photographs by Gerald Cubitt.

Chapter 4

A useful general history of Malaya in the larger context of Southeast Asia is found in D. R. Sardesai, *Southeast Asia: Past and Present* (Boulder, CO: Westview Press, 1989), which also contains an excellent bibliography. Similar in coverage, and highly readable, is Lea E. Williams, *Southeast Asia: A History* (New York: Oxford University Press, 1976).

Leonard Y. Andaya and Barbara Watson Andaya, *A History of Malaysia* (London: Macmillan, 1982), is a thorough general study of Malaysia from early times to about 1980.

Three more specialized volumes on the early history of Malaysia include Paul Wheatley, *The Golden Khersonese: Studies in the Historical Geography of the Malay Peninsula Before A.D. 1500* (Kuala Lumpur: University of Malaya Press, 1966); K. N. Chaudhuri, *Trade and Civilisation in the Indian Ocean* (Cambridge and New York: Cambridge University Press, 1985), which deals with the Malay world in the larger context of the spread of Indian and Islamic civilization and the coming of the Europeans; and Anthony Reid, *Southeast Asia in the Age of Commerce, 1450–1680* (New Haven: Yale University Press, 1988), which is particularly good on issues of culture and daily life.

Chapter 5

Sir Frank Swettenham, *British Malaya* (London: George Allen & Unwin Ltd., 1955) provides an excellent perspective on the British experience in Malaya from the point of view of a former colonial official.

C. D. Cowan, *Nineteenth Century Malaya* (London: Oxford University Press, 1961) covers some of the same ground as Swettenham, but from a broader point of view.

Victor Purcell, *The Chinese in Malaya* (London: Oxford University Press, 1948) is the classic work in its field.

For northern Borneo, two excellent books deal with the British colonial period. Steven Runciman, *The White Rajahs* (Cambridge: Cambridge University Press, 1960) tells the story of the Brooke Dynasty of Sarawak; Kennedy G. Tregonning, *Under Chartered Company Rule* (Singapore: University of Malaya Press, 1958) deals with Sabah under the British North Borneo Company.

The Ranee of Sarawak, *My Life in Sarawak* (London: Methuen & Co., Ltd., 1913) is a fascinating personal memoir by the wife of Sarawak's second "White Rajah"; Henri Fauconnier, *The Soul of Malaya* (London: E. Mathews and Marrot, 1931) is an equally fascinating anecdotal study of white-planter society in Malaya.

Many of Somerset Maugham's Southeast Asian tales are found in two collections of his short stories, *The Casuarina Tree* (New York: George H. Doran Co., 1926) and *Ah King* (London: Wm. Heinemann, Ltd., 1933).

Chapter 6

William Roff, *The Origins of Malay Nationalism* (New Haven: Yale University Press, 1967), traces the rise of nationalism through an examination of modern Malay literature and culture.

Anthony Short, *The Communist Insurrection in Malaya, 1948–1960* (New York: Crane, Russak, 1975) is a good account of the Emergency, based in part on official documents.

Stanley S. Bedlington, *Malaysia and Singapore: The Building of New States* (Ithaca, NY: Cornell University Press, 1978) is a comprehensive study of decolonization in Malaysia, covering Singapore and Brunei as well as the Malay Peninsula, Sarawak, and Sabah.

Tan Sri Mohamed Suffian bin Hashim, *An Introduction to the Constitution of Malaysia* (Kuala Lumpur: Government Printing Office, 1972), by a noted Malaysian judge, gives a detailed account of Malaysia's government based on an analysis of the country's constitution.

Chapter 7

Mahathir bin Mohamad, *The Malay Dilemma* (Singapore: Donald Moore, 1970). This
outspoken look at ethnic politics in Malaysia by the country's current Prime Minister was banned in Malaysia for many years on the grounds that it was too controver-
sial.

S. Husin Ali, *The Malays: Their Problems and Future* (Kuala Lumpur: Heineman/Asia,
1983) gives an interesting perspective on modern Malaysia, emphasizing class
rather than ethnicity.

V. S. Naipaul, *Among the Believers: An Islamic Journey* (New York: Alfred A. Knopf,
Inc., 1981), gives a strongly critical view of the rise of Islamic orthodoxy in
Malaysian society.

Kua Kit Soong, ed., *National Culture and Democracy* (Kuala Lumpur, 1985) is a
collection of essays debating the issue of Islam and ethnicity in Malaysia's national
culture.

Though it deals with Indonesia rather than with Malaysia, Wanda Warming and
Michael Gaworski, *The World of Indonesian Textiles* (London: Serindia Publications,
1981), has an excellent discussion of *ikat* and *batik* and of the role of textiles in
Malay society that applies to Malaysia as well.

Chapter 8

For Malaysia's traditional culture, see Richard Winstedt, *The Malays: A Cultural
History* (1947; rev. ed., Singapore: Graham Brash, 1981). During his long career
Winstedt wrote many other books on Malay history, literature, and culture, includ-
ing the classic *The Circumstances of Malay Life* (1909; reprint edition, New York:
AMS Press, 1981).

The *Asian Theatre Journal*, published quarterly, regularly includes articles on the
performing arts in Malaysia and elsewhere in the Malay world.

A good source of information on Malaysian film and performing arts is the Department
of Performances, Films, and Lectures of The Asia Society, 725 Park Avenue, New
York, NY 10021.

Chapter 9

The cartoons of Lat (Mohamad Nor Khalid) have been published in two book-length collections, *Kampung Boy* (Kuala Lumpur: Kampung Boy Sendirian Berhad, 1986), and *Mat Som* (Kuala Lumpur: Kampung Boy Sendirian Berhad, 1989), and appear regularly in the Kuala Lumpur newspaper *The New Straits Times*—the feature pages of which are an excellent source of information on contemporary daily life in Malaysia. The humorous cartoon essays of another Malaysian graphic artist, Kit Lee, are collected in *Adoi* ["Ouch!"], (Kuala Lumpur, 1989); they provide a wonderful view of urban life and contemporary fads.

In "Huckleberry Finn on the South China Sea" (*Focus on Asian Studies*, Vol. VI, No. 1, Fall 1987, pp. 14–17), Carol Laderman describes the role of young children in a Malay fishing village in helping to put food on the table. In the same issue of *Focus on Asian Studies*, pp. 18–19, Bill Albert has collected some "Malay Fruit Proverbs" that illuminate attitudes toward food and life.

Chapter 10

A fine up-to-date account of contemporary Malaysian politics, economics, and society is found in R. S. Milne and Diane K. Mauzy, *Malaysia: Tradition, Modernity, and Islam* (Boulder, CO: Westview Press, 1986).

Thomas Sowell, *Preferential Policies: An International Perspective* (New York: William Morrow, and Company, Inc., 1990), compares the New Economic Policy of Malaysia with affirmative-action programs in the United States, Nigeria, India, and elsewhere, and finds that all have failed to achieve their goals.

A brief factual introduction to modern Brunei is found in *Salamat Datang/Welcome* (Bandar Seri Begawan: Government Printing Office, n.d.). Two recent biographies of the Sultan of Brunei are Baron Arthur Gwynne Jones Chalfont, *By God's Will: A Portrait of the Sultan of Brunei* (London: Weidenfeld and Nicolson, 1989) and James Bartholomew, *The Richest Man in the World: The Sultan of Brunei* (London: Viking, 1989). The former is a respectful treatment produced with official cooperation, while the latter is scathingly critical.

The best source of current information on events in Malaysia and Brunei is Asia's best newsweekly, *The Far Eastern Economic Review*, published in Hong Kong. *FEER* also publishes the annual *Asia Yearbook*, with summaries of essential information on politics, economics, and foreign relations for all the countries of East, Southeast, and South Asia.

Index*

Numbers in *italics* refer to illustrations.

*Several terms that appear throughout the text are not included in this index. For Malaya and Malaysia, see the Table of Contents. For Chinese, Indians, and Malays, see the Table of Contents and also entries under "Ethnic issues" and "Language" in this index.

Baba-Nyonya culture, 118–19,
    188–89, *208*
Badminton, 180
Bajau, 3, *9*, 16, 18, 22–23, 111
Bali, 68, 82, 168
Bamboo, 64, 66–67, 162, 175, 198
Bandar Seri Begawan, 30, 47, 58, *59*,
    136, 186, 227, *228–29*
Bangkok, 77
Bantam, 92
Baram River, 197
Barisan Nasional, 125, 141–43
Batak, 77
Batavia, 91, 94, 96–97
Batik, 68, 151, 152–55, *153*, 176,
    197
Beeswax, 35, 69, 152, 175
Bencoolen, 92, 94–96
Bendahara, 83
Bidayuh, 16, 22
Bintulu, 47
Birch, J.W.W., 108
Birds' nests, 47–48, 69
Bolkiah V, Sultan, 64, 83
Borneo Company, Ltd., 98
Borobudur, 63, *71*, 73–75, *74*
Briggs Plan, 130
British Commonwealth, 135,
    224–25
British East India Company, 64, 86,
    92, 95–96, 101, 106
British North Borneo Company, 93,
    105, 111, 129, *136*
British Protectorates, *105*, 110–11
Bronze Age, 66
Brooke, Charles Vyner, 128
Brooke, Sir James, 93, 97–101, *99*
Brooke Dynasty, Sarawak, 54, 95–101,
    99, *105*, 128

Brooke, Sir Charles Johnson, 100,
    101
Brunei
    as British Protectorate, 93, 105,
        111, 122, 129
    and Brooke Dynasty of Sarawak, 93,
        95–98
    contemporary issues, 185–87, 218,
        226–33
    early history, 64, 82–83, 85,
        88–89, 91
    economy and resources, *47*, *59*, 123,
        126, 230–31
    ethnic groups and languages, 8, 11,
        18, 22, 102–3
    geography and climate, *6*, 25,
        29–30, 32, 48, 59
    independence of, 124–25, 137
    Islam in, 82, *136*, 145, *228–29*,
        233
Brunei, Sultan of. *See* Haji Hassanal
    Bolkiah
Brunei Shell Corporation, 52, 186
Buddhism, 13, 71–74
Bugis, 3, 77, 92, 117
Bumiputras, 8–9, 14, 54, 184, 200–1,
    203, 205, 213, 220
Buruma, Ian, 14, 170
Butterworth, 58

Cameron Highlands, 32
Cannon, bronze, *85*, 89, 176
Capsicum (chili) peppers, 41–42,
    188–89
Carpenter, Frank G., 58, 112,
    117
Cheongsam, 158

ABOUT THE AUTHOR

John S. Major is a Senior Editor at the Book-of-the-Month club. Since earning his doctorate in Asian Studies at Harvard, he has been a professor at Dartmouth College; a program director at the Asia Society; a frequent visitor to Bali, Java, Malaysia, and Brunei; and the author of Land and People books on China and Mongolia.